TASHA TUDOR'S
FAVORITE STORIES

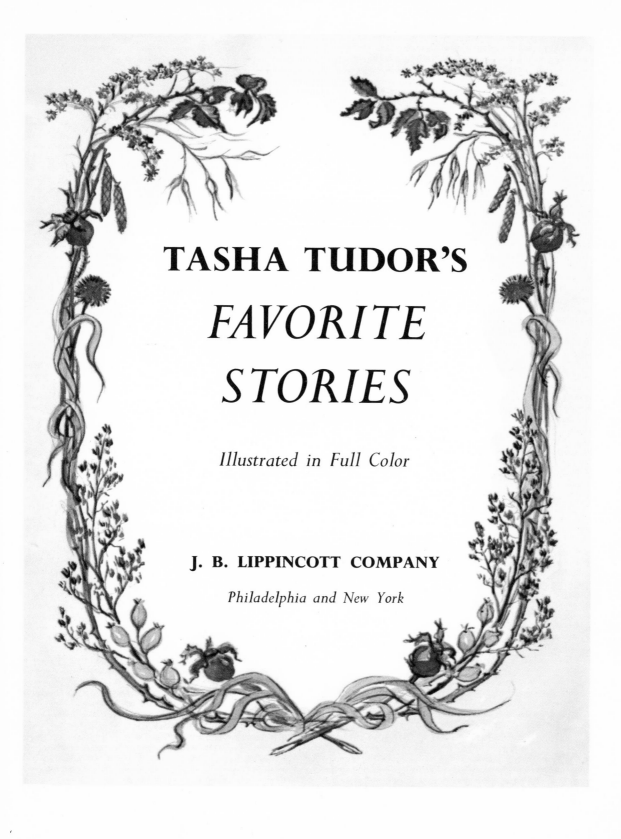

TASHA TUDOR'S
FAVORITE STORIES

Illustrated in Full Color

J. B. LIPPINCOTT COMPANY

Philadelphia and New York

ACKNOWLEDGMENTS

Thanks go to the following publishers, agents, and individuals for their kind permission to reprint material copyrighted or controlled by them:

Doubleday and Company, Inc., Mrs. George Bambridge, and the Macmillan Company of Canada, Ltd. for "The Cat That Walked by Himself" from *Just So Stories* by Rudyard Kipling.

Houghton Mifflin Company for "Wicked John and the Devil" from *Grandfather Tales* by Richard Chase, copyright 1948 by Houghton Mifflin Company.

Harold Ober Associates for "The Little Dressmaker" from *The Little Bookroom* by Eleanor Farjeon, copyright © 1955 by Eleanor Farjeon, published by Henry Z. Walck, Inc.

To Virginia Lightner

CONTENTS

CONTENTS

TASHA TUDOR'S
FAVORITE
STORIES

THE CAT THAT WALKED BY HIMSELF

RUDYARD KIPLING

HEAR and attend and listen; for this befell and behappened and became and was, O my Best Beloved, when the Tame animals were wild. The Dog was wild, and the Horse was wild, and the Cow was wild, and the Sheep was wild, and the Pig was wild—as wild as wild could be—and they walked in the Wet Wild Woods by their wild lones. But the wildest of all the wild animals was the Cat. He walked by himself, and all places were alike to him.

Of course the Man was wild too. He was dreadfully wild. He didn't even begin to be tame till he met the Woman, and she told him that she did not like living in his wild ways. She picked out a nice dry Cave, instead of a heap of wet leaves, to lie down in; and she strewed clean sand on the floor; and she lit a nice fire of wood at the back of the Cave; and she hung a dried wild-horse skin, tail-down, across the opening of the Cave; and she said, 'Wipe your feet, dear, when you come in, and now we'll keep house.'

That night, Best Beloved, they ate wild sheep roasted on the hot stones, and flavoured with wild garlic and wild pepper; and wild duck stuffed with wild rice and wild fenugreek and wild coriander; and marrow-bones of wild oxen; and wild cherries, and wild grenadillas. Then the Man went to sleep in front of the fire ever so happy; but the Woman sat up, combing her hair. She took the bone of the shoulder of mutton—the big fat blade-bone—and she looked at the wonderful marks on it, and she threw more wood on the fire, and she made a Magic. She made the First Singing Magic in the world.

Out in the Wet Wild Woods all the wild animals gathered together where they could see the light of the fire a long way off, and they wondered what it meant.

Then Wild Horse stamped with his wild foot and said, 'O my Friends and O my Enemies, why have the Man and the Woman made that great light in that great Cave, and what harm will it do us?'

Wild Dog lifted up his wild nose and smelled the smell of roast mutton, and said, 'I will go up and see and look, and say; for I think it is good. Cat, come with me.'

'Nenni!' said the Cat. 'I am the Cat who walks by himself, and all places are alike to me. I will not come.'

'Then we can never be friends again,' said Wild Dog, and he trotted off to the Cave. But when he had gone a little way the Cat said to himself, 'All places are alike to me. Why should I not go too and see and look and come away at my own liking.' So he slipped after Wild Dog softly, very softly, and hid himself where he could hear everything.

When Wild Dog reached the mouth of the Cave he lifted up the dried horse-skin with his nose and sniffed the beautiful smell of the roast mutton, and the Woman, looking at the blade-bone, heard him, and laughed, and said, 'Here comes the first. Wild Thing out of the Wild Woods, what do you want?'

Wild Dog said, 'O my Enemy and Wife of my Enemy, what is this that smells so good in the Wild Woods?'

Then the Woman picked up a roasted mutton-bone and threw it to Wild Dog, and said, 'Wild Thing out of the Wild Woods, taste and try.' Wild Dog gnawed the bone, and it was more delicious than anything he had ever tasted, and he said, 'O my Enemy and Wife of my Enemy, give me another.'

The Woman said, 'Wild Thing out of the Wild Woods, help my Man to hunt through the day and guard this Cave at night, and I will give you as many roast bones as you need.'

'Ah!' said the Cat, listening. 'This is a very wise Woman, but she is not so wise as I am.'

Wild Dog crawled into the Cave and laid his head on the Woman's lap, and said, 'O my Friend and Wife of my Friend, I will help your Man to hunt through the day, and at night I will guard your Cave.'

'Ah!' said the Cat, listening. 'That is a very foolish Dog.' And he went back through the Wet Wild Woods waving his wild tail, and walking by his wild lone. But he never told anybody.

When the Man woke up he said, 'What is Wild Dog doing here?' And the Woman said, 'His name is not Wild Dog any more, but the First Friend, because he will be our friend for always and always and always. Take him with you when you go hunting.'

Next night the Woman cut great green armfuls of fresh grass

from the water-meadows, and dried it before the fire, so that it smelt like new-mown hay, and she sat at the mouth of the Cave and plaited a halter out of horse-hide, and she looked at the shoulder of mutton-bone—at the big broad blade-bone—and she made a Magic. She made the Second Singing Magic in the world.

Out in the Wild Woods all the wild animals wondered what had happened to Wild Dog, and at last Wild Horse stamped with his foot and said, 'I will go and see and say why Wild Dog has not returned. Cat, come with me.'

'Nenni!' said the Cat. 'I am the Cat who walks by himself, and all places are alike to me. I will not come.' But all the same he followed Wild Horse softly, very softly, and hid himself where he could hear everything.

When the Woman heard Wild Horse tripping and stumbling on his long mane, she laughed and said, 'Here comes the second. Wild Thing out of the Wild Woods, what do you want?'

Wild Horse said, 'O my Enemy and Wife of my Enemy, where is Wild Dog?'

The Woman laughed, and picked up the blade-bone and looked at it, and said, 'Wild Thing out of the Wild Woods, you did not come here for Wild Dog, but for the sake of this good grass.'

And Wild Horse, tripping and stumbling on his long mane, said, 'That is true; give it me to eat.'

The Woman said, 'Wild Thing out of the Wild Woods, bend your wild head and wear what I give you, and you shall eat the wonderful grass three times a day.'

'Ah,' said the Cat, listening, 'this is a clever Woman, but she is not so clever as I am.'

Wild Horse bent his wild head, and the Woman slipped the plaited hide halter over it, and Wild Horse breathed on the

Woman's feet and said, 'O my Mistress, and Wife of my Master, I will be your servant for the sake of the wonderful grass.'

'Ah,' said the Cat, listening, 'that is a very foolish Horse.' And he went back through the Wet Wild Woods, waving his wild tail and walking by his wild lone. But he never told anybody.

When the Man and the Dog came back from hunting, the Man said, 'What is Wild Horse doing here?' And the Woman said, 'His name is not Wild Horse any more, but the First Servant, because he will carry us from place to place for always and always and always. Ride on his back when you go hunting.'

Next day, holding her wild head high that her wild horns should not catch in the wild trees, Wild Cow came up to the Cave, and the Cat followed, and hid himself just the same as before; and everything happened just the same as before; and the Cat said the same things as before, and when Wild Cow had promised to give her milk to the Woman every day in exchange for the wonderful grass, the Cat went back through the Wet Wild Woods waving his wild tail and walking by his wild lone, just the same as before. But he never told anybody. And when the Man and the Horse and the Dog came home from hunting and asked the same questions same as before, the Woman said, 'Her name is not Wild Cow any more, but the Giver of Good Food. She will give us the warm white milk for always and always and always, and I will take care of her while you and the First Friend and the First Servant go hunting.'

Next day the Cat waited to see if any other Wild thing would go up to the Cave, but no one moved in the Wet Wild Woods, so the Cat walked there by himself; and he saw the Woman milking the Cow, and he saw the light of the fire in the Cave, and he smelt the smell of the warm white milk.

Cat said, 'O my Enemy and Wife of my Enemy, where did Wild Cow go?'

The Woman laughed and said, 'Wild Thing out of the Wild Woods, go back to the Woods again, for I have braided up my hair, and I have put away the magic blade-bone, and we have no more need of either friends or servants in our Cave.'

Cat said, 'I am not a friend, and I am not a servant. I am the Cat who walks by himself, and I wish to come into your cave.'

Woman said, 'Then why did you not come with First Friend on the first night?'

Cat grew very angry and said, 'Has Wild Dog told tales of me?'

Then the Woman laughed and said, 'You are the Cat who walks by himself, and all places are alike to you. You are neither a friend nor a servant. You have said it yourself. Go away and walk by yourself in all places alike.'

Then Cat pretended to be sorry and said, 'Must I never come into the Cave? Must I never sit by the warm fire? Must I never drink the warm white milk? You are very wise and very beautiful. You should not be cruel even to a Cat.'

Woman said, 'I knew I was wise, but I did not know I was beautiful. So I will make a bargain with you. If ever I say one word in your praise you may come into the Cave.'

'And if you say two words in my praise?' said the Cat.

'I never shall,' said the Woman, 'but if I say two words in your praise, you may sit by the fire in the Cave.'

'And if you say three words?' said the Cat.

'I never shall,' said the Woman, 'but if I say three words in your praise, you may drink the warm white milk three times a day for always and always and always.'

Then the Cat arched his back and said, 'Now let the Curtain at the mouth of the Cave, and the Fire at the back of the Cave, and the Milk-pots that stand beside the Fire, remember what my Enemy and the Wife of my Enemy has said.' And he went away through the Wet Wild Woods waving his wild tail and walking by his wild lone.

That night when the Man and the Horse and the Dog came home from hunting, the Woman did not tell them of the bargain that she had made with the Cat, because she was afraid that they might not like it.

Cat went far and far away and hid himself in the Wet Wild Woods by his wild lone for a long time till the Woman forgot all about him. Only the Bat—the little upside-down Bat—that hung inside the Cave, knew where Cat hid; and every evening Bat would fly to Cat with news of what was happening.

One evening Bat said, 'There is a Baby in the Cave. He is new and pink and fat and small, and the Woman is very fond of him.'

'Ah,' said the Cat, listening, 'but what is the Baby fond of?'

'He is fond of things that are soft and tickle,' said the Bat. 'He is fond of warm things to hold in his arms when he goes to sleep. He is fond of being played with. He is fond of all those things.'

'Ah,' said the Cat, listening, 'then my time has come.'

Next night Cat walked through the Wet Wild Woods and hid very near the Cave till morning-time, and Man and Dog and Horse went hunting. The Woman was busy cooking that morning, and the Baby cried and interrupted. So she carried him outside the Cave and gave him a handful of pebbles to play with. But still the Baby cried.

Then the Cat put out his paddy paw and patted the Baby on the cheek, and it cooed; and the Cat rubbed against its fat knees and tickled it under its fat chin with his tail. And the Baby laughed and the Woman heard him and smiled.

Then the Bat—the little upside-down Bat—that hung in the

mouth of the Cave said, 'O my Hostess and Wife of my Host and Mother of my Host's Son, a Wild Thing from the Wild Woods is most beautifully playing with your Baby.'

'A blessing on that Wild Thing whoever he may be,' said the Woman, straightening her back, 'for I was a busy woman this morning and he has done me a service.'

The very minute and second, Best Beloved, the dried horse-skin Curtain that was stretched tail-down at the mouth of the Cave fell down—*woosh!*—because it remembered the bargain she had made with the Cat, and when the Woman went to pick it up—lo and behold!—the Cat was sitting quite comfy inside the Cave.

'O my Enemy and Wife of my Enemy and Mother of my Enemy,' said the Cat, 'it is I: for you have spoken a word in my praise, and now I can sit within the Cave for always and always and always. But still I am the Cat who walks by himself, and all places are alike to me.'

The Woman was very angry, and shut her lips tight and took up her spinning-wheel and began to spin.

But the Baby cried because the Cat had gone away, and the Woman could not hush it, for it struggled and kicked and grew black in the face.

'O my Enemy and Wife of my Enemy and Mother of my Enemy,' said the Cat, 'take a strand of the wire that you are spinning and tie it to your spinning-whorl and drag it along the floor, and I will show you a magic that shall make your Baby laugh as loudly as he is now crying.'

'I will do so,' said the Woman, 'because I am at my wits' end; but I will not thank you for it.'

She tied the thread to the little clay spindle-whorl and drew it across the floor, and the Cat ran after it and patted it with his paws

She tied the thread to the little clay spindle-whorl
and drew it across the floor.

and rolled head over heels, and tossed it backward over his shoulder and chased it between his hind-legs and pretended to lose it, and pounced down upon it again, till the Baby laughed as loudly as it had been crying, and scrambled after the Cat and frolicked all over the Cave till it grew tired and settled down to sleep with the Cat in its arms.

'Now,' said the Cat, 'I will sing the Baby a song that shall keep him asleep for an hour.' And he began to purr, loud and low, low and loud, till the Baby fell fast asleep. The Woman smiled as she looked down upon the two of them and said, 'That was wonderfully done. No question but you are very clever, O Cat.'

That very minute and second, Best Beloved, the smoke of the fire at the back of the Cave came down in clouds from the roof— *puff!*—because it remembered the bargain she had made with the Cat, and when it had cleared away—lo and behold!—the Cat was sitting quite comfy close to the fire.

'O my Enemy and Wife of my Enemy and Mother of my Enemy,' said the Cat, 'it is I, for you have spoken a second word in my praise, and now I can sit by the warm fire at the back of the Cave for always and always and always. But still I am the Cat who walks by himself, and all places are alike to me.'

Then the Woman was very very angry, and let down her hair and put more wood on the fire and brought out the broad blade-bone of the shoulder of mutton and began to make a Magic that should prevent her from saying a third word in praise of the Cat. It was not a Singing Magic, Best Beloved, it was a Still Magic; and by and by the Cave grew so still that a little wee-wee mouse crept out of a corner and ran across the floor.

'O my Enemy and Wife of my Enemy and Mother of my Enemy,' said the Cat, 'is that little mouse part of your magic?'

'Ouh! Chee! No indeed!' said the Woman, and she dropped the blade-bone and jumped upon the footstool in front of the fire and braided up her hair very quick for fear that the mouse should run up it.

'Ah,' said the Cat, watching, 'then the mouse will do me no harm if I eat it?'

'No,' said the Woman, braiding up her hair, 'eat it quickly and I will ever be grateful to you.'

Cat made one jump and caught the little mouse, and the Woman said, 'A hundred thanks. Even the First Friend is not quick enough to catch little mice as you have done. You must be very wise.'

That very moment and second, O Best Beloved, the Milk-pot that stood by the fire cracked in two pieces—*ffft*—because it remembered the bargain she had made with the Cat, and when the Woman jumped down from the footstool—lo and behold!—the Cat was lapping up the warm white milk that lay in one of the broken pieces.

'O my Enemy and Wife of my Enemy and Mother of my Enemy,' said the Cat, 'it is I; for you have spoken three words in my praise, and now I can drink the warm white milk three times a day for always and always and always. But *still* I am the Cat who walks by himself, and all places are alike to me.'

Then the Woman laughed and set the Cat a bowl of the warm white milk and said, 'O Cat, you are as clever as a man, but remember that your bargain was not made with the Man or the Dog, and I do not know what they will do when they come home.'

'What is that to me?' said the Cat. 'If I have my place in the Cave by the fire and my warm white milk three times a day I do not care what the Man or the Dog can do.'

That evening when the Man and the Dog came into the Cave, the Woman told them all the story of the bargain while the Cat sat by the fire and smiled. Then the Man said, 'Yes, but he has not made a bargain with *me* or with all proper Men after me.' Then he took off his two leather boots and he took up his little stone axe (that makes three) and he fetched a piece of wood and a hatchet (that is five altogether), and he set them out in a row and he said, 'Now we will make *our* bargain. If you do not catch mice when you are in the Cave for always and always and always, I will throw these five things at you whenever I see you, and so shall all proper Men do after me.'

'Ah,' said the Woman, listening, 'this is a very clever Cat, but he is not so clever as my Man.'

The Cat counted the five things (and they looked very knobby) and he said, 'I will catch mice when I am in the Cave for always and always and always; but *still* I am the Cat who walks by himself, and all places are alike to me.'

'Not when I am near,' said the Man. 'If you had not said that last I would have put all these things away for always and always and always; but I am now going to throw my two boots and my little stone axe (that makes three) at you whenever I meet you. And so shall all proper Men do after me!'

Then the Dog said, 'Wait a minute. He has not made a bargain with *me* or with all proper Dogs after me.' And he showed his teeth and said, 'If you are not kind to the Baby while I am in the Cave for always and always and always, I will hunt you till I catch you, and when I catch you I will bite you. And so shall all proper Dogs do after me.'

'Ah,' said the Woman, listening, 'this is a very clever Cat, but he is not so clever as the Dog.'

Cat counted the Dog's teeth (and they looked very pointed) and he said, 'I will be kind to the Baby while I am in the Cave, as long as he does not pull my tail too hard, for always and always and always. But *still* I am the Cat that walks by himself, and all places are alike to me.'

'Not when I am near,' said the Dog. 'If you had not said that last I would have shut my mouth for always and always and always; but *now* I am going to hunt you up a tree whenever I meet you. And so shall all proper Dogs do after me.'

Then the Man threw his two boots and his little stone axe (that makes three) at the Cat, and the Cat ran out of the Cave and the Dog chased him up a tree; and from that day to this, Best Beloved, three proper Men out of five will always throw things at a Cat whenever they meet him, and all proper Dogs will chase him up a tree. But the Cat keeps his side of the bargain too. He will kill mice and he will be kind to Babies when he is in the house, just as long as they do not pull his tail too hard. But when he has done that, and between times, and when the moon gets up and night comes, he is the Cat that walks by himself, and all places are alike to him. Then he goes out to the Wet Wild Woods or up the Wet Wild Trees or on the Wet Wild Roofs, waving his wild tail and walking by his wild lone.

From *Just So Stories*
by Rudyard Kipling

A FALLING OUT

KENNETH GRAHAME

HAROLD told me the main facts of this episode some time later,—in bits and with reluctance. It was not a recollection he cared to talk about. The crude blank misery of a moment is apt to leave a dull bruise which is slow to depart, if it ever do so entirely; and Harold confesses to a twinge or two, still, at times, like the veteran who brings home a bullet inside him from martial plains over sea.

He knew he was a brute the moment he had done it. Selina had not meant to worry, only to comfort and assist. But his soul was one raw sore within him, when he found himself shut up in the schoolroom after hours, merely for insisting that 7 times 7 amounted to 47. The injustice of it seemed so flagrant. Why not 47 as much as 49! One number was no prettier than the other to look at, and it was evidently only a matter of arbitrary taste and preference, and, anyhow, it had always been 47 to him, and would be to the end of time. So when Selina came in out of the sun, leaving the Trappers of the Far West behind her, and putting off the glory of being an Apache squaw in order to hear him his tables and win his release, Harold turned on her venomously, rejected her kindly overtures, and even drove his elbow into her sympathetic ribs, in his determination to be left alone in the glory of sulks. The fit passed directly, his eyes were opened, and his soul sat in the dust as he sorrowfully began to cast about for some atonement heroic enough to salve the wrong.

Of course poor Selina looked for no sacrifice nor heroics whatever; she didn't even want him to say he was sorry. If he would only make it up, she would have done the apologising part herself. But that was not a boy's way. Something solid, Harold felt, was due from him; and until that was achieved, making-up must not be thought of, in order that the final effect might not be spoilt. Accordingly, when his release came, and Selina hung about trying to catch his eye, Harold, possessed by the demon of a distorted motive, avoided her steadily—though he was bleeding inwardly at every minute of delay—and came to me instead. Needless to say, I warmly approved his plan. It was so much more high-toned than just going and making-up tamely, which any one could do; and a girl who had been jobbed in the ribs by a hostile elbow could not be expected for a moment to overlook it, without the liniment of an offering to soothe her injured feelings.

'I know what she wants most,' said Harold. 'She wants that set of tea-things in the toy-shop window, with the red and blue flowers on 'em; she's wanted it for months, 'cos her dolls are getting big enough to have real afternoon tea; and she wants it so badly that she won't walk that side of the street when we go into the town. But it costs five shillings!'

Then we set to work seriously, and devoted the afternoon to a realisation of assets and the composition of a Budget that might have been dated without shame from Whitehall. The result worked out as follows:—

	s. d.
By one uncle, unspent through having been lost for nearly a week—turned up at last in the straw of the dog-kennel	2 6
By advance from me on security of next uncle, and failing that, to be called in at Christmas	1 0
By shaken out of missionary-box with the help of a knife-blade. (They were our own pennies and a forced levy)	0 4
By bet due from Edward, for walking across the field where Farmer Larkin's bull was, and Edward bet him twopence he wouldn't—called in with difficulty	0 2
By advance from Martha, on no security at all, only you mustn't tell your aunt . . .	1 0
Total	5 0

and at last we breathed again.

The rest promised to be easy. Selina had a tea-party at five on the morrow, with the chipped old wooden tea-things that had served her successive dolls from babyhood. Harold would slip off directly after dinner, going alone, so as not to arouse suspicion, as we were not allowed to go into the town by ourselves. It was nearly two miles to our small metropolis, but there would be plenty of time for him to go and return, even laden with the olive-branch neatly packed in shavings. Besides, he might meet the butcher, who was his friend and would give him a lift. Then, finally, at five, the rapture of the new tea-service, descended from the skies; and, retribution made, making-up at last, without loss of dignity. With the event before us, we thought it a small thing that twenty-four hours more of alienation and pretended sulks must be kept up on Harold's part; but Selina, who naturally knew nothing of the treat in store for her, moped for the rest of the evening, and took a very heavy heart to bed.

Next day when the hour for action arrived, Harold evaded Olympian attention with an easy modesty born of long practice, and made off for the front gate. Selina, who had been keeping her eye upon him, thought he was going down to the pond to catch frogs, a joy they had planned to share together, and made after him. But Harold, though he heard her footsteps, continued sternly on his high mission, without even looking back; and Selina was left to wander disconsolately among flower-beds that had lost—for her—all scent and colour. I saw it all, and, although cold reason approved our line of action, instinct told me we were brutes.

Harold reached the town—so he recounted afterwards—in record time, having run most of the way for fear the tea-things, which had reposed six months in the window, should be snapped up by some other conscience-stricken lacerator of a sister's feelings; and it seemed hardly credible to find them still there, and their owner willing to part with them for the price marked on the ticket. He paid his money down at once, that there should be no drawing back from the bargain; and then, as the things had to be taken out of the window and packed, and the afternoon was yet young, he thought he might treat himself to a taste of urban joys and the *vie de Boheme*. Shops came first, of course, and he flattened his nose successively against the window with the indiarubber balls in it, and the clock-work locomotive; and against the barber's window, with wigs on blocks, reminding him of uncles, and shaving-cream that looked so good to eat; and the grocer's window, displaying more currants than the whole British population could possibly consume without a special effort; and the window of the bank, wherein gold was thought so little of that it was dealt about in shovels. Next there was the market-place, with all its clamorous joys; and when a runaway calf came down the street like a cannon-ball, Harold felt that he had not lived in vain. The whole place was so brimful of excitement that he had quite forgotten the why and the wherefore of his being there, when a sight of the church clock recalled him to his better self, and sent him flying out of the town, as he realised he had only just time enough left to get back in. If he were after his appointed hour, he would not only miss his high triumph, but probably would be detected as a transgressor of bounds—a crime before which a private opinion on multiplication sank to nothingness. So he jogged along on his homeward way, thinking of many things, and probably talking to himself a good deal, as his habit was. He had covered nearly half the distance, when suddenly—a deadly sinking in the pit of his stomach—a paralysis of every limb—around him a world extinct of light and music—a black sun and a reeling sky—he had forgotten the tea-things!

It was useless, it was hopeless, all was over and nothing could now be done. Nevertheless he turned and ran back wildly, blindly, choking with the big sobs that evoked neither pity nor comfort from a merciless mocking world around; a stitch in his side, dust in his eyes, and black despair clutching at his heart. So he stumbled on, with leaden legs and bursting sides, till—as if Fate had not yet dealt him her last worst buffet of all—on turning a corner in the road he almost ran under the wheels of a dog-cart, in which, as it pulled up, was apparent the portly form of Farmer Larkin, the arch-enemy, at whose ducks he had been shying stones that very morning!

Harold could only stand and blubber hopelessly.

Had Harold been in his right and unclouded senses, he would have vanished through the hedge some seconds earlier, rather than pain the farmer by any unpleasant reminiscences which his appearance might recall; but, as things were, he could only stand and blubber hopelessly, caring, indeed, little now what further misery might befall him. The farmer, for his part, surveyed the desolate figure with some astonishment, calling out in no unfriendly accents, 'Why, Master Harold! whatever be the matter? Baint runnin' away, be ee?'

Then Harold, with the unnatural courage born of desperation, flung himself on the step, and, climbing into the cart, fell in the straw at the bottom of it, sobbing out that he wanted to go back, go back! The situation had a vagueness; but the farmer, a man of action rather than of words, swung his horse round smartly, and they were in the town again by the time Harold had recovered himself sufficiently to furnish details. As they drove up to the shop, the woman was waiting at the door with the parcel; and hardly a minute seemed to have elapsed since the black crisis, ere they were bowling along swiftly home, the precious parcel hugged in a close embrace.

And now the farmer came out in quite a new and unexpected light. Never a word did he say of broken fences and hurdles, of trampled crops and harried flocks and herds. One would have thought the man had never possessed a head of live stock in his life. Instead, he was deeply interested in the whole dolorous quest of the tea-things, and sympathised with Harold on the disputed point in mathematics as if he had been himself at the same stage of education. As they neared home, Harold found himself, to his surprise, sitting up and chatting to his new friend like man to man; and before he was set down at a convenient gap in the garden hedge, he had promised that when Selina gave her first public tea-party, little Miss Larkin should be invited to come and bring her whole sawdust family along with her; and the farmer appeared as pleased and proud as if he had won a gold medal at the Agricultural Show, and really, when I heard the story, it began to dawn upon me that those Olympians must have certain good points, far down in them, and that I should have to leave off abusing them some day.

At the hour of five, Selina, having spent the afternoon searching for Harold in all his accustomed haunts, sat down disconsolately to tea with her dolls, who ungenerously refused to wait beyond the appointed hour. The wooden tea-things seemed more chipped than usual; and the dolls themselves had more of wax and sawdust, and less of human colour and intelligence about them, than she ever remembered before. It was then that Harold burst in, very dusty, his stockings at his heels, and the channels ploughed by tears still showing on his grimy cheeks; and Selina was at last permitted to know that he had been thinking of her ever since his ill-judged exhibition of temper, and that his sulks had not been the genuine article, nor had he gone frogging by himself. It was a very happy hostess who dispensed hospitality that evening to a glassy-eyed stiff-kneed circle; and many a dollish *gaucherie*, that would have been severely checked on ordinary occasions, was as much overlooked as if it had been a birthday.

But Harold and I, in what I was afterwards given to understand was our stupid masculine way, thought all her happiness sprang from the possession of the long-coveted tea-service.

From *The Golden Age*
by Kenneth Grahame

RAGGYLUG
The Story of a Cottontail Rabbit

ERNEST THOMPSON SETON

RAGGYLUG, or Rag, was the name of a young cottontail rabbit. It was given him from his torn and ragged ear, a life-mark that he got in his first adventure. He lived with his mother in Olifant's swamp, where I made their acquaintance and gathered, in a hundred different ways, the little bits of proof and scraps of truth that at length enabled me to write this history.

Those who do not know the animals well may think I have humanized them, but those who have lived so near them as to know somewhat of their ways and their minds will not think so.

Truly rabbits have no speech as we understand it, but they have a way of conveying ideas by a system of sounds, signs, scents, whisker-touches, movements, and example that answers the purpose of speech; and it must be remembered that though in telling this story I freely translate from rabbit into English, *I repeat nothing that they did not say.*

I

The rank swamp grass bent over and concealed the snug nest where Raggylug's mother had hidden him. She had partly covered him with some of the bedding, and, as always, her last warning was to 'lay low and say nothing, whatever happens.' Though tucked in bed, he was wide awake and his bright eyes were taking in that part of his little green world that was straight above. A bluejay and a red-squirrel, two notorious thieves, were loudly berating each other for stealing, and at one time Rag's home bush was the centre of their fight; a yellow warbler caught a blue butterfly but six inches from his nose, and a scarlet and black ladybug, serenely waving her knobbed feelers, took a long walk up one grassblade, down another, and across the nest and over Rag's face—and yet he never moved nor even winked.

After a while he heard a strange rustling of the leaves in the near thicket. It was an odd, continuous sound, and though it went this way and that way and came ever nearer, there was no patter of feet with it. Rag had lived his whole life in the Swamp (he was three weeks old) and yet had never heard anything like this. Of course his curiosity was greatly aroused. His mother had cautioned him to lay low, but that was understood to be in case of danger, and this strange sound without footfalls could not be anything to fear.

The low rasping went past close at hand, then to the right, then back, and seemed going away. Rag felt he knew what he was about; he wasn't a baby; it was his duty to learn what it was. He slowly raised his roly-poly body on his short fluffy legs, lifted his little round head above the covering of his nest and peeped out into the woods. The sound had ceased as soon as he moved. He saw nothing, so took one step forward to a clear view, and instantly found himself face to face with an enormous Black Serpent.

"Mammy," he screamed in mortal terror as the monster darted at him. With all the strength of his tiny limbs he tried to run. But in a flash the Snake had him by one ear and whipped around him with his coils to gloat over the helpless little baby bunny he had secured for dinner.

"Mam-my—Mam-my," gasped poor little Raggylug as the cruel monster began slowly choking him to death. Very soon the little one's cry would have ceased, but bounding through the woods straight as an arrow came Mammy. No longer a shy, helpless little Molly Cottontail, ready to fly from a shadow: the mother's love was strong in her. The cry of her baby had filled her with the courage of a hero, and—hop, she went over that horrible reptile. Whack, she struck down at him with her sharp hind claws as she passed, giving him such a stinging blow that he squirmed with pain and hissed with anger.

"M-a-m-m-y," came feebly from the little one. And Mammy came leaping again and again and struck harder and fiercer until the loathsome reptile let go the little one's ear and tried to bite the old one as she leaped over. But all he got was a mouthful of wool each time, and Molly's fierce blows began to tell, as long bloody rips were torn in the Black Snake's scaly armor.

Things were now looking bad for the Snake; and bracing himself for the next charge, he lost his tight hold on Baby Bunny, who at once wriggled out of the coils and away into the underbrush, breathless and terribly frightened, but unhurt save that his left ear was much torn by the teeth of that dreadful Serpent.

Molly now had gained all she wanted. She had no notion of fighting for glory or revenge. Away she went into the woods and the little one followed the shining beacon of her snow-white tail until she led him to a safe corner of the Swamp.

II

Old Olifant's Swamp was a rough, brambly tract of second-growth woods, with a marshy pond and a stream through the middle. A few ragged remnants of the old forest still stood in it and a few of the still older trunks were lying about as dead logs in the brushwood. The land about the pond was of that willow-grown sedgy kind that cats and horses avoid, but that cattle do not fear. The drier zones were overgrown with briars and young trees. The outermost belt of all, that next the fields, was of thrifty, gummy-trunked young pines whose living needles in air and dead ones on earth offer so delicious an odor to the nostrils of the passer-by, and so deadly a breath to those seedlings that would compete with them for the worthless waste they grow on.

All around for a long way were smooth fields, and the only wild tracks that ever crossed these fields were those of a thoroughly bad and unscrupulous fox that lived only too near.

The chief indwellers of the swamp were Molly and Rag. Their nearest neighbors were far away, and their nearest kin were dead. This was their home, and here they lived together, and here Rag received the training that made his success in life.

Molly was a good little mother and gave him a careful bringing up. The first thing he learned was 'to lay low and say nothing.' His adventure with the snake taught him the wisdom of this. Rag never forgot that lesson; afterward he did as he was told, and it made the other things come more easily.

The second lesson he learned was 'freeze.' It grows out of the first, and Rag was taught it as soon as he could run.

'Freezing' is simply doing nothing, turning into a statue. As soon as he finds a foe near, no matter what he is doing, a well-trained Cottontail keeps just as he is and stops all movement, for the creatures of the woods are of the same color as the things in the woods and catch the eye only while moving. So when enemies chance together, the one who first sees the other can keep himself unseen by 'freezing' and thus have all the advantage of choosing the time for attack or escape. Only those who live in the woods know the importance of this; every wild creature and every hunter must learn it; all learn to do it well, but not one of them can beat Molly Cottontail in the doing. Rag's mother taught him this trick by example. When the white cotton cushion that she always carried to sit on went bobbing away through the woods, of course Rag ran his hardest to keep up. But when Molly stopped and 'froze,' the natural wish to copy made him do the same.

But the best lesson of all that Rag learned from his mother was the secret of the Brierbrush. It is a very old secret now, and to make it plain you must first hear why the Brierbrush quarrelled with the beasts.

Long ago the Roses used to grow on bushes that had no thorns. But the Squirrels and Mice used to climb after them, the Cattle used to knock them off with their horns, the Possum would twitch them off with his long tail, and the Deer, with his sharp hoofs, would break them down. So the Brierbrush armed itself with spikes to protect its roses and declared eternal war on all creatures that climbed trees, or had horns, or hoofs, or long tails. This left the Brierbrush at peace with none but Molly Cottontail, who could not climb, was hornless, hoofless, and had scarcely any tail at all.

In truth the Cottontail had never harmed a Brierrose, and having now so many enemies the Rose took the Rabbit into special friend-

ship, and when dangers are threatening poor Bunny he flies to the nearest Brierbrush, certain that it is ready with a million keen and poisoned daggers to defend him.

So the secret that Rag learned from his mother was, 'The Brierbrush is your best friend.'

Much of the time that season was spent in learning the lay of the land, and the bramble and brier mazes. And Rag learned them so well that he could go all around the swamp by two different ways and never leave the friendly briers at any place for more than five hops.

It is not long since the foes of the Cottontails were disgusted to find that man had brought a new kind of bramble and planted it in long lines throughout the country. It was so strong that no creatures could break it down, and so sharp that the toughest skin was torn by it. Each year there was more of it and each year it became a more serious matter to the wild creatures. But Molly Cottontail had no fear of it. She was not brought up in the briers for nothing. Dogs and foxes, cattle and sheep, and even man himself might be torn by those fearful spikes: but Molly understands it and lives and thrives under it. And the further it spreads the more safe country there is for the Cottontail. And the name of this new and dreaded bramble is—*the barbed-wire fence.*

III

Molly had no other children to look after now, so Rag had all her care. He was unusually quick and bright as well as strong, and he had uncommonly good chances; so he got on remarkably well.

All the season she kept him busy learning the tricks of the trail, and what to eat and drink and what not to touch. Day by day she worked to train him; little by little she taught him, putting into his mind hundreds of ideas that her own life or early training had stored in hers, and so equipped him with the knowledge that makes life possible to their kind.

Close by her side in the clover-field or the thicket he would sit and copy her when she wobbled her nose 'to keep her smeller clear,' and pull the bite from her mouth or taste her lips to make sure he was getting the same kind of fodder. Still copying her, he learned to comb his ears with his claws and to dress his coat and to bite the burrs out of his vest and socks. He learned, too, that nothing but clear dewdrops from the briers were fit for a rabbit to drink, as water which has once touched the earth must surely bear some taint. Thus he began the study of woodcraft, the oldest of all sciences.

As soon as Rag was big enough to go out alone, his mother taught him the signal code. Rabbits telegraph each other by thumping on the ground with their hind feet. Along the ground sound carries far; a thump that at six feet from the earth is not heard at twenty yards will, near the ground, be heard at least one hundred yards. Rabbits have very keen hearing, and so might hear this same thump at two hundred yards, and that would reach from end to end of Olifant's Swamp. A single *thump* means 'look out' or 'freeze.' A slow *thump thump* means 'come.' A fast *thump thump* means 'danger'; and a very fast *thump thump thump* means 'run for dear life.'

At another time, when the weather was fine and the bluejays were quarrelling among themselves, a sure sign that no dangerous foe was about, Rag began a new study. Molly, by flattening her ears, gave the sign to squat. Then she ran far away in the thicket

and gave the thumping signal for 'come.' Rag set out at a run to
the place but could not find Molly. He thumped, but got no reply.
Setting carefully about his search he found her foot-scent and
following this strange guide, that the beasts all know so well and
man does not know at all, he worked out the trail and found her
where she was hidden. Thus he got his first lesson in trailing, and
thus it was that the games of hide and seek they played became the
schooling for the serious chase of which there was so much in his
after life.

Before that first season of schooling was over he had learnt
all the principal tricks by which a rabbit lives and in not a few
problems showed himself a veritable genius.

He was an adept at 'tree,' 'dodge,' and 'squat,' he could play
'log-lump,' with 'wind' and 'baulk' with 'back-track' so well that
he scarcely needed any other tricks. He had not yet tried it, but he
knew just how to play 'barb-wire,' which is a new trick of the
brilliant order; he had made a special study of 'sand,' which burns
up all scent, and he was deeply versed in 'change-off,' 'fence,' and
'double' as well as 'hole-up,' which is a trick requiring longer
notice, and yet he never forgot that 'lay-low' is the beginning of
all wisdom and 'brierbush' the only trick that is always safe.

He was taught the signs by which to know all his foes and then
the way to baffle them. For hawks, owls, foxes, hounds, curs,
minks, weasels, cats, skunks, coons, and men, each have a different
plan of pursuit, and for each and all of these evils he was taught
a remedy.

And for knowledge of the enemy's approach he learnt to depend
first on himself and his mother, and then on the bluejay. "Never
neglect the bluejay's warning," said Molly; "he is a mischief-
maker, a marplot, and a thief all the time, but nothing escapes him.

40

He wouldn't mind harming us, but he cannot, thanks to the briers, and his enemies are ours, so it is well to heed him. If the wood-pecker cries a warning you can trust him, he is honest; but he is a fool beside the bluejay, and though the bluejay often tells lies for mischief you are safe to believe him when he brings ill news."

The barb-wire trick takes a deal of nerve and the best of legs. It was long before Rag ventured to play it, but as he came to his full powers it became one of his favorites.

"It's fine play for those who can do it," said Molly. "First you lead off your dog on a straightaway and warm him up a bit by nearly letting him catch you. Then keeping just one hop ahead, you lead him at a long slant full tilt into a breast-high barb-wire. I've seen many a dog and fox crippled, and one big hound killed outright this way. But I've also seen more than one rabbit lose his life in trying it."

Rag early learnt what some rabbits never learn at all, that 'hole-up' is not such a fine ruse as it seems; it may be the certain safety of a wise rabbit, but soon or late is a sure deathtrap to a fool. A young rabbit always thinks of it first, an old rabbit never tries it till all others fail. It means escape from a man or dog, a fox or a bird of prey, but it means sudden death if the foe is a ferret, mink, skunk, or weasel.

There were but two ground-holes in the Swamp. One on the Sunning Bank, which was a dry sheltered knoll in the South-end. It was open and sloping to the sun, and here on fine days the Cotton-tails took their sunbaths. They stretched out among the fragrant pine needles and winter-green in odd cat-like positions, and turned slowly over as though roasting and wishing all sides well done. And they blinked and panted, and squirmed as if in dreadful pain; yet this was one of the keenest enjoyments they knew.

Just over the brow of the knoll was a large pine stump. Its grotesque roots wriggled out above the yellow sand-bank like dragons, and under their protecting claws a sulky old woodchuck had digged a den long ago. He became more sour and ill-tempered as weeks went by, and one day waited to quarrel with Olifant's dog instead of going in so that Molly Cottontail was able to take possession of the den an hour later.

This, the pine-root hole, was afterward very coolly taken by a self-sufficient young skunk who with less valor might have enjoyed greater longevity, for he imagined that even man with a gun would fly from him. Instead of keeping Molly from the den for good, therefore, his reign, like that of a certain Hebrew king, was over in seven days.

The other, the fern-hole, was in a fern thicket next the clover field. It was small and damp, and useless except as a last retreat. It also was the work of a woodchuck, a well-meaning friendly neighbor, but a hare-brained youngster whose skin in the form of a whip-lash was now developing higher horse-power in the Olifant working team.

"Simple justice," said the old man, "for that hide was raised on stolen feed that the team would a' turned into horse-power anyway."

The Cottontails were now sole owners of the holes, and did not go near them when they could help it, lest anything like a path should be made that might betray these last retreats to an enemy.

There was also the hollow hickory, which, though nearly fallen, was still green, and had the great advantage of being open at both ends. This had long been the residence of one Lotor, a solitary old coon whose ostensible calling was frog-hunting, and who, like the monks of old, was supposed to abstain from all flesh food. But it was shrewdly suspected that he needed but a chance to indulge in a diet of rabbit. When at last one dark night he was killed while raiding Olifant's hen-house, Molly, so far from feeling a pang of regret, took possession of his cosy nest with a sense of unbounded relief.

IV

Bright August sunlight was flooding the Swamp in the morning. Everything seemed soaking in the warm radiance. A little brown swamp-sparrow was teetering on a long rush in the pond. Beneath him there were open spaces of dirty water that brought down a few scraps of the blue sky, and worked it and the yellow duck-weed into an exquisite mosaic, with a little wrong-side picture of the bird in the middle. On the bank behind was a great vigorous growth of golden green skunk-cabbage, that cast dense shadow over the brown swamp tussocks.

The eyes of the swamp-sparrow were not trained to take in the color glories, but he saw what we might have missed; that two of the numberless leafy brown bumps under the broad cabbage-leaves were furry living things, with noses that never ceased to move up and down whatever else was still.

It was Molly and Rag. They were stretched under the skunk-cabbage, not because they liked its rank smell, but because the winged ticks could not stand it at all and so left them in peace.

Rabbits have no set time for lessons, they are always learning; but what the lesson is depends on the present stress, and that must arrive before it is known. They went to this place for a quiet rest, but had not been long there when suddenly a warning note from the ever-watchful bluejay caused Molly's nose and ears to go up and her tail to tighten to her back. Away across the Swamp was Olifant's big black and white dog, coming straight toward them.

"Now," said Molly, "squat while I go and keep that fool out of mischief." Away she went to meet him and she fearlessly dashed across the dog's path.

"Bow-ow-ow," he fairly yelled as he bounded after Molly, but she kept just beyond his reach and led him where the million daggers struck fast and deep, till his tender ears were scratched raw, and guided him at last plump into a hidden barbed-wire fence, where he got such a gashing that he went homeward howling with pain. After making a short double, a loop and a baulk in case the dog should come back, Molly returned to find that Rag in his eagerness was standing bolt upright and craning his neck to see the sport.

This disobedience made her so angry that she struck him with her hind foot and knocked him over in the mud.

One day as they fed on the near clover field a red-tailed hawk came swooping after them. Molly kicked up her hind legs to make fun of him and skipped into the briers along one of their old pathways, where of course the hawk could not follow. It was the main path from the Creekside Thicket to the Stove-pipe brush-pile. Several creepers had grown across it, and Molly, keeping one eye on the hawk, set to work and cut the creepers off. Rag watched her, then ran on ahead, and cut some more that were across the path. "That's right," said Molly, "always keep the runways clear, you will need them often enough. Not wide, but clear. Cut everything like a creeper across them and some day you will find you have cut a snare." "A what?" asked Rag, as he scratched his right ear with his left hind foot.

"A snare is something that looks like a creeper, but it doesn't grow and it's worse than all the hawks in the world," said Molly, glancing at the now far-away red-tail, "for there it hides night and day in the runway till the chance to catch you comes."

"I don't believe it could catch me," said Rag, with the pride of youth as he rose on his heels to rub his chin and whiskers high up on a smooth sapling. Rag did not know he was doing this, but his mother saw and knew it was a sign, like the changing of a boy's voice, that her little one was no longer a baby but would soon be a grown-up Cottontail.

V

There is magic in running water. Who does not know it and feel it? The railroad builder fearlessly throws his bank across the wide bog or lake, or the sea itself, but the tiniest rill of running water he treats with great respect, studies its wish and its way and gives it all it seems to ask. The thirst-parched traveller in the poisonous alkali deserts holds back in deadly fear from the sedgy ponds till he finds one down whose centre is a thin, clear line, and a faint flow, the sign of running, living water, and joyfully he drinks.

There is magic in running water, no evil spell can cross it. Tam O'Shanter proved its potency in time of sorest need. The wild-wood creature with its deadly foe following tireless on the trail scent, realizes its nearing doom and feels an awful spell. Its strength is spent, its every trick is tried in vain till the good Angel leads it to the water, the running, living water, and dashing in it follows the cooling stream, and then with force renewed takes to the woods again.

There is magic in running water. The hounds come to the very spot and halt and cast about; and halt and cast in vain. Their spell is broken by the merry stream, and the wild thing lives its life.

And this was one of the great secrets that Raggylug learned from his mother—"after the Brierrose, the Water is your friend."

One hot, muggy night in August, Molly led Rag through the woods. The cotton-white cushion she wore under her tail twinkled ahead and was his guiding lantern, though it went out as soon as she stopped and sat on it. After a few runs and stops to listen, they came to the edge of the pond. The hylas in the trees above them were singing '*sleep, sleep*,' and away out on a sunken log in the deep water, up to his chin in the cooling bath, a bloated bullfrog was singing the praises of a '*jug o' rum*.'

"Follow me still," said Molly, in rabbit, and 'flop' she went into the pond and struck out for the sunken log in the middle. Rag flinched but plunged with a little 'ouch,' gasping and wobbling his nose very fast but still copying his mother. The same movements as on land sent him through the water, and thus he found he could swim. On he went till he reached the sunken log and scrambled up by his dripping mother on the high dry end, with a rushy screen around them and the Water that tells no tales. After this in warm black nights when that old fox from Springfield came prowling through the Swamp, Rag would note the place of the bullfrog's voice, for in case of direst need it might be a guide to safety. And thenceforth the words of the song that the bullfrog sang were, '*Come, come, in danger come*.'

This was the latest study that Rag took up with his mother—it was really a post-graduate course, for many little rabbits never learn it at all.

Rag flinched but plunged with a little 'ouch.'

VI

No wild animal dies of old age. Its life has soon or late a tragic end. It is only a question of how long it can hold out against its foes. But Rag's life was proof that once a rabbit passes out of his youth he is likely to outlive his prime and be killed only in the last third of life, the downhill third we call old age.

The Cottontails had enemies on every side. Their daily life was a series of escapes. For dogs, foxes, cats, skunks, coons, weasels, minks, snakes, hawks, owls, and men, and even insects were all plotting to kill them. They had hundreds of adventures, and at least once a day they had to fly for their lives and save themselves by their legs and wits.

More than once that hateful fox from Springfield drove them to taking refuge under the wreck of a barbed-wire hog-pen by the spring. But once there they could look calmly at him while he spiked his legs in vain attempts to reach them.

Once or twice Rag when hunted had played off the hound against a skunk that had seemed likely to be quite as dangerous as the dog.

Once he was caught alive by a hunter who had a hound and a ferret to help him. But Rag had the luck to escape next day, with a yet deeper distrust of ground holes. He was several times run into the water by the cat, and many times was chased by hawks and owls, but for each kind of danger there was a safeguard. His mother taught him the principal dodges, and he improved on them and made many new ones as he grew older. And the older and wiser he grew the less he trusted to his legs, and the more to his wits for safety.

Ranger was the name of a young hound in the neighborhood.

To train him his master used to put him on the trail of one of the Cottontails. It was nearly always Rag that they ran, for the young buck enjoyed the runs as much as they did, the spice of danger in them being just enough for zest. He would say:

"Oh, mother! here comes the dog again, must have a run to-day."

"You are too bold, Raggy, my son!" she might reply. "I fear you will run once too often."

"But, mother, it is such glorious fun to tease that fool dog, and it's all good training. I'll thump if I am too hard pressed, then you can come and change off while I get my second wind."

On he would come, and Ranger would take the trail and follow till Rag got tired of it. Then he either sent a thumping telegram for help, which brought Molly to take charge of the dog, or he got rid of the dog by some clever trick. A description of one of these shows how well Rag had learned the arts of the woods.

He knew that his scent lay best near the ground, and was strongest when he was warm. So if he could get off the ground, and be left in peace for half an hour to cool off, and for the trail to stale, he knew he would be safe. When, therefore, he tired of the chase, he made for the Creekside brier-patch, where he 'wound' —that is, zigzagged—till he left a course so crooked that the dog was sure to be greatly delayed in working it out. He then went straight to D in the woods, passing one hop to windward of the high log E. Stopping at D, he followed his back trail to F, here he leaped aside and ran toward G. Then, returning on his trail to J, he waited till the hound passed on his trail at I. Rag then got back on his old trail at H, and followed it to F, where, with a scent-baulk or great leap aside, he reached the high log, and running to its higher end, he sat like a bump.

Ranger lost much time in the bramble maze, and the scent was very poor when he got it straightened out, and came to D. Here he began to circle to pick it up, and after losing much time, struck the trail which ended suddenly at G. Again he was at fault, and had to circle to find the trail. Wider and wider the circles, until at last, he passed right under the log Rag was on. But a cold scent, on a cold day, does not go downward much. Rag never budged nor winked, and the hound passed.

Again the dog came round. This time he crossed the low part of the log, and stopped to smell it. 'Yes, clearly it was rabbity,' but it was a stale scent now; still he mounted the log.

It was a trying moment for Rag, as the great hound came sniff-sniffing along the log. But his nerve did not forsake him; the wind was right; he had his mind made up to bolt as soon as Ranger came half way up. But he didn't come. A yellow cur would have seen the rabbit sitting there, but the hound did not, and the scent seemed stale, so he leaped off the log, and Rag had won.

VII

Old Olifant had doubtless a right to burn all those brush-piles in the east and south of the Swamp and to clear up the wreck of the old barbed-wire hog-pen just below the spring. But it was none the less hard on Rag and his mother. The first were their various residences and outposts, and the second their grand fastness and safe retreat.

They had so long held the Swamp and felt it to be their very own in every part and suburb,—including Olifant's grounds and buildings—that they would have resented the appearance of another rabbit even about the adjoining barnyard.

Their claim, that of long, successful occupancy, was exactly the same as that by which most nations hold their land, and it would be hard to find a better right.

During the time of the January thaw the Olifants had cut the rest of the large wood about the pond and curtailed the Cottontails' domain on all sides. But they still clung to the dwindling Swamp, for it was their home and they were loath to move to foreign parts. Their life of daily perils went on, but they were still fleet of foot, long of wind, and bright of wit. Of late they had been somewhat troubled by a mink that had wandered up-stream to their quiet nook. A little judicious guidance had transferred the uncomfortable visitor to Olifant's hen-house. But they were not yet quite sure that he had been properly looked after. So for the present they gave up using the ground-holes, which were, of course, dangerous blind-alleys, and stuck closer than ever to the briers and the brush-piles that were left.

That first snow had quite gone and the weather was bright and warm until now. Molly, feeling a touch of rheumatism, was somewhere in the lower thicket seeking a teaberry tonic. Rag was sitting in the weak sunlight on a bank in the east side. The smoke from the familiar gable chimney of Olifant's house came fitfully drifting a pale blue haze through the underwoods and showing as a dull brown against the brightness of the sky. The sun-gilt gable was cut off midway by the banks of brierbrush, that purple in shadow shone like rods of blazing crimson and gold in the light. Beyond the house the barn with its gable and roof, new gilt as the house, stood up like a Noah's ark.

The sounds that came from it, and yet more the delicious smell that mingled with the smoke, told Rag that the animals were being fed cabbage in the yard. Rag's mouth watered at the idea of the feast. He blinked and blinked as he snuffed its odorous promises, for he loved cabbage dearly. But then he had been to the barnyard the night before after a few paltry clover-tops, and no wise rabbit would go two nights running to the same place.

Therefore he did the wise thing. He moved across where he could not smell the cabbage and made his supper of a bundle of hay that had been blown from the stack. Later, when about to settle for the night, he was joined by Molly, who had taken her teaberry and then eaten her frugal meal of sweet birch near the Sunning Bank.

Meanwhile the sun had gone about his business elsewhere, taking all his gold and glory with him. Off in the east a big black shutter came pushing up and rising higher and higher; it spread over the whole sky, shut out all light and left the world a very gloomy place indeed. Then another mischief-maker, the wind, taking advantage of the sun's absence, came on the scene and set about brewing trouble. The weather turned colder and colder; it seemed worse than when the ground had been covered with snow.

"Isn't this terribly cold? How I wish we had our stove-pipe brush-pile," said Rag.

"A good night for the pine-root hole," replied Molly, "but we have not yet seen the pelt of that mink on the end of the barn, and it is not safe till we do."

The hollow hickory was gone—in fact at this very moment its trunk, lying in the wood-yard, was harboring the mink they feared. So the Cottontails hopped to the south side of the pond and, choosing a brush-pile, they crept under and snuggled down for the night, facing the wind but with their noses in different directions so as to go out different ways in case of alarm. The wind blew harder and colder as the hours went by, and about midnight a fine icy snow came ticking down on the dead leaves and hissing through the brush heap. It might seem a poor night for hunting, but that old fox from Springfield was out. He came pointing up the wind in the shelter of the Swamp and chanced in the lee of the brush-pile, where he scented the sleeping Cottontails. He halted for a moment, then came stealthily sneaking up toward the brush under which his nose told him the rabbits were crouching. The noise of the wind and the sleet enabled him to come quite close before Molly heard the faint crunch of a dry leaf under his paw. She touched Rag's whiskers, and both were fully awake just as the fox sprang on them; but they always slept with their legs ready for a jump. Molly darted out into the blinding storm. The fox missed his spring but followed like a racer, while Rag dashed off to one side.

There was only one road for Molly; that was straight up the wind, and bounding for her life she gained a little over the unfrozen mud that would not carry the fox, till she reached the margin of the pond. No chance to turn now, on she must go.

Splash! splash! through the weeds she went, then plunge into the deep water.

And plunge went the fox close behind. But it was too much for Reynard on such a night. He turned back, and Molly, seeing only one course, struggled through the reeds into the deep water and struck out for the other shore. But there was a strong headwind. The little waves, icy cold, broke over her head as she swam, and the water was full of snow that blocked her way like soft ice, or floating mud. The dark line of the other shore seemed far, far away, with perhaps the fox waiting for her there.

But she laid her ears flat to be out of the gale, and bravely put forth all her strength with wind and tide against her. After a long, weary swim in the cold water, she had nearly reached the farther reeds when a great mass of floating snow barred her road; then the wind on the bank made strange, fox-like sounds that robbed her of all force, and she was drifted far backward before she could get free from the floating bar.

Again she struck out, but slowly—oh so slowly now. And when at last she reached the lee of the tall reeds, her limbs were numbed, her strength spent, her brave little heart was sinking, and she cared no more whether the fox were there or not. Through the reeds she did indeed pass, but once in the weeds her course wavered and slowed, her feeble strokes no longer sent her landward, the ice forming around her, stopped her altogether. In a little while the cold, weak limbs ceased to move, the furry nose-tip of the little mother Cottontail wobbled no more, and the soft brown eyes were closed in death.

But there was no fox waiting to tear her with ravenous jaws. Rag had escaped the first onset of the foe, and as soon as he regained his wits he came running back to change-off and so help his mother. He met the old fox going round the pond to meet Molly and led him far and away, then dismissed him with a barbed-wire gash on his head, and came to the bank and sought about and trailed and thumped, but all his searching was in vain; he could not find his little mother. He never saw her again, and he never knew whither she went, for she slept her never-waking sleep in the ice-arms of her friend the Water that tells no tales.

Poor little Molly Cottontail! She was a true heroine, yet only one of unnumbered millions that without a thought of heroism have lived and done their best in their little world, and died. She fought a good fight in the battle of life. She was good stuff; the stuff that never dies. For flesh of her flesh and brain of her brain was Rag. She lives in him, and through him transmits a finer fibre to her race.

And Rag still lives in the Swamp. Old Olifant died that winter, and the unthrifty sons ceased to clear the Swamp or mend the wire fences. Within a single year it was a wilder place than ever; fresh trees and brambles grew, and falling wires made many Cottontail castles and last retreats that dogs and foxes dared not storm. And there to this day lives Rag. He is a big strong buck now and fears no rivals. He has a large family of his own, and a pretty brown wife that he got I know not where. There, no doubt, he and his children's children will flourish for many years to come, and there you may see them any sunny evening if you have learnt their signal code, and choosing a good spot on the ground, know just how and when to thump it.

From *Wild Animals I Have Known*
by Ernest Thompson Seton

WICKED JOHN AND THE DEVIL

RICHARD CHASE

ONE TIME there was an old blacksmith that folks called Wicked John. They say he was right mean: never would join the church, never did go to meetin', always laughed about folks gettin' saved and bein' baptized and sech. One thing about him, though, mean as he was, he always did treat a stranger right. And one mornin' a old beggar came along: crippled up, walkin' on two sticks, all bent over with rheumatism, looked right tired and hungry-like. Stood there in the door, and Wicked John fin'lly hollered at him, says, "Come on in! Whyn't ye come on in and sit down?" So the old beggar he heaved over the doorsill, sat down on it, and they talked a while. Wicked John kept right on workin', talkin' big, and directly he threw his hammer down and went to the house. Come back with a big plate of vittles: boiled sweet potato, big chunk of ham-meat, greens, beans, big slice of cake, and a glass of sweet milk. Says, "Here, old man! You might make out with these rations—if there's anything here you can eat."

The old beggar thanked him and started in eatin', and old John he went on with his work. Well, he was a-hammerin' around over there, sort of watchin' the beggar man, and pretty soon he saw him lay that plate and the glass to one side and start to get up. He let them two sticks fall to the ground and commenced straightenin' up, straightenin' up, and all the kinks come out of him, till the next thing Wicked John knowed, a big stout-lookin' man was r'ared up there in the door: had a long white beard and white hair, white robe right down to his feet, and a big key in his hand. Old John had done dropped his hammer and was a-standin' there with his mouth hangin' open and his eyes popped out. So the old man says to him, says, "Well, John, I'm Saint Peter. Yes, that's who I am, and once every year I walk the earth to see can I find any decent folks left down here, and the first man treats me right I always give him three wishes. So you can just go ahead now and take your three wishes. Anything you've a mind to, you can just wish for it and hit'll be that-a-way."

Wicked John looked over there at Saint Peter sort of grinnin' like he didn't think it was really so, says, "Well, Peter, you better let me study on it a minute. Three wishes. Aaa Lord!"

Looked around, started wishin' on the first thing popped into his head. He didn't care!

"Well now, I've got a fine old high-back rockin' chair there by the door, and when I get my work done up I like to sit in my rocker; but, don't you know, every day nearly, blame if there ain't somebody done gone and got there ahead of me—one of these loafers hangs around in here of a evenin'. Makes me mad! And I just wish:—that anybody sits in my old rocker would have to stay there and rock right on till I let 'em get up.

"Aaa Lord!—Lemme see now.—Well, there's my old sledge hammer. It's these blame boys come in here and get to messin' with it, take it out there across the road, see how big a rock they can bust; and—con-found!—if I don't have to go out there ever' time I need it and hunt for it where them feisty boys have done gone and dropped it down in the grass somewhere. And I jest wish:— that *any*body teches my sledge hammer would have to pound with it, and keep right on a-poundin' till I let 'em stop."

Well, Saint Peter he looked kind of sorry like he thought old John was a-wastin' his wishes pretty bad, but that old blacksmith he was mean, like I said, just didn't care about nothin' or nobody. Looked around at Saint Peter right mischievous-like, grinned sort of devilish, says, "One more wish, huh? Well, all right. Now:— I got a fine thornbush jest outside the door there, fire bush, gets full of red blooms real early in the spring of the year; and I like my old fire thorn, but—con-found!—ever'body comes here to get their horses shoed, blame if they don't tromple all over that bush, back their wagons into it, break it down; and—Aaa Lord!—these highfalutin' folks comes over the mountain a-fox-huntin'— Humph! fox-huntin' in red coats!—looks like they jest got to have ridin' switches off my bush, break off ridin' switches ever' time they pass. And I jest wish:—anybody *teches* my fire thorn, it 'uld catch 'em and hold 'em right down in the middle of all them stickers till I let 'em out."

Well, Saint Peter he stepped over the doorsill and he was gone from there and Wicked John couldn't tell which-a-way he went nor nothin'.

So that old blacksmith he kept on blacksmithin' in his black-smith shop, and it wasn't long till John and his old woman they got to fussin'. Well, she was jawin' at him and jawin' at him, and he jawed right back at her, till fin'lly she told him, says, "The Devil take ye anyhow, old man! I jest *wish he would!*"

So that day the old man was a-workin' in his shop, looked up and there was a little devil a-standin' in the door, says, "Daddy said he'd take ye now. Said for me to bring ye right on back."

"All right, son. I'll be ready to go with ye in jest a few more licks. Reckon you can let me finish this horseshoe. Come on in. I'll not be but a minute or two."

Well, the little devil he stepped over in the shop, hung around awhile, and then he went straight and sat down in that old high-back rockin' chair, commenced rockin'. Wicked John he finished the horseshoe, soused it in the coolin' tub, throwed it on the ground and picked him up another'n.

"Hey, old man! You said jest finish that one!" And he tried to get out of that rocker, but the more he tried to get up the worse that old chair rocked him, till that little devil's head was just a-goin' *whammity-bang!* against the chairback. And fin'lly he got to beggin' and hollerin' for Wicked John to let him go.

"All right. I'll let ye go if you get on out of here and not bother me no more."

So the little devil said yes, he'd go, and when the chair quit rockin', he jumped out of it and—*a-whippity-cut!* out the door he flew.

Well, not long after that the old woman she lit into the old man again about somethin' or other; and they was a-havin' it! She was just a-fussin', and he was just a-laughin' at her, till fin'lly she stomped around, says, "I'll jest tell ye, old man! The Devil can have ye right now for all I care! He shore can! He can send for ye and take ye off from here, and the sooner the better. That's all there are to it now!" Stomped on out to the kitchen, slammed the door.

So that day another little devil come to the door of the shop, little bigger'n the first 'un, says, "Come on, old man. Daddy sent me for ye. Said for me not to wait for nothin', bring ye right on back. So come on now, and we'll go."

"All right, son. Yes, in-deed. I'm jest about ready. Come in, and I know you'll let me hit a few more licks on this wagon-tire. I'm bound to finish hit 'fore we start."

Well, that little devil he come on inside the shop, got to hangin' around lookin' at what old John was doin', seen he was havin' it kind of awkward the way he had to hold on to that wagon tire and beat it with one hand, says, "Here, old man, you hold it and let me beat it. We got to hurry or Daddy'll get after me for stayin' so long."—Picked up that old sledge hammer layin' there on the ground, started in poundin'.

So Wicked John he held the wagon tire up and turned it where he wanted it fixed, and when it was done he pulled it out from under the hammer between licks, set it against the wall. And when the little devil tried to let go the hammer handle, he just stuck to it and hit a-poundin' right on. Well, the way the old sledge swung that little devil around in there, a-jerkin' him up and down with his legs a-flyin' ever' which-a-way—hit was a sight in this world! So he got to beggin', "Please let me go! Please, sir! Make this thing turn loose of me!"

"All right. I'll let ye go if you get on out of here and don't never come back. Ye hear?'

The little devil said yes, he heard and no, he'd not be back never no more; and then he fell off the hammer-handle and out the door he streaked.

Well, a few days after that the old woman she started raisin' another racket. They hadn't spoke many words 'fore she r'ared back and stuck her hands on her hips, hollered at him, says, "Old man! I jest wish—the *puore—old—Devil* himself would come on and git ye! I shore do! Now you get on out of here 'fore I knock ye in the head with this stick of firewood!"

So old John he dodged the stick of wood and laughed at the old lady, and went on out to his shop, and—sure enough—he hadn't any more'n got started workin' 'fore he looked up and there standin' in the door was the Old Boy himself, with his horns and his tail and that old cow's foot of his'n propped up on the sill, says, "COME ON NOW, OLD MAN! AND I AIN'T A-GOIN' TO TAKE NO FOOLISHNESS OFF YE NEITHER!"

"Yes, sir! No, sir! I'm ready to go, mister, right now. I jest got to finish sharpenin' this mattick. Promised a man I'd get it done first thing this mornin'. Come on in and sit down."

"NO! I'LL NOT SIT IN NO CHAIR OF YOUR'N!"

"All right, sir. All right. We'll be ready to go quicker'n you can turn around if you'd jest give this mattick blade a lick or two while I hold it here. There's the sledge-hammer leanin' there on the doorsill."

"NO! I AIN'T GOIN' TO TECH NO SLEDGE HAM-MER!" says the old Devil. Says, "YOU DONE MADE ME MAD ENOUGH ALREADY, OLD MAN! I DIDN'T LIKE A BIT THE WAY YOU DONE MY BOYS, AND I'M A-TAKIN' YOU OFF FROM HERE RIGHT NOW. YOU HEARD ME!"

And the old Devil reached in and grabbed Wicked John by the back of his collar, started draggin' him out. So old John he started in fightin': punchin', knockin', beatin', poundin', scratchin', kickin', bitin'. They had several rounds there just outside the

Standin' in the door was the Old Boy himself, with his horns and his tail and that old cow's foot of his'n.

door, made the old Devil awful mad, says, "CONFOUND YE, OLD MAN! I'M GOIN' TO LICK THE HIDE OFF YOU RIGHT NOW. JEST SEE IF I DON'T—WHERE'LL I GET ME A SWITCH?"

The old Devil looked around and reached for that bush, and time he touched it, hit grabbed him and wropped around him, jerked him headforemost right down in the middle of that bush where them thorns was the thickest. The old Devil he tried to get loose but the more he thrashed around in there, the worse he got scratched up till fin'lly he just stayed right still, with his legs a-stickin' out the top of the bush.

"Mister?"

"What ye want?"

"Please, sir, let me out of here."

"All right. I'll let ye go on one condition:—you, and none of your boys, don't none of ye never come up here a-botherin' me no more. Ye hear? You promise me that and I might let ye go."

"Heck yes, I'll promise," says the old Devil. "I'll not come, and I'll not send nobody neither—not never no more."

So the bush turned him loose, and sech a kickin' up dust you never did see. The Old Boy left there and he wasn't moseyin' neither.

Well, Wicked John he kept on blacksmithin' and he wasn't bothered by no more devils. And after a long time he died and went on up to the pearly gates. When he got there he knocked, and Saint Peter opened up a little crack, looked out, says, "Oh, it's you, is it? What ye want?"

"Well," old John told him, "I thought I might stand *some* little show of gettin' in up here."

"You? Why, old man, don't you know we got your record in yonder? I'll tell ye right now: I was lookin' at your accounts just the other day; and on the credit side—yes—you have a few entries 'way up at the top of the page; but over on the other side—why, man! hit's filled up right down to the bottom line. There hain't a chance in the world of you gettin' in this place." And Saint Peter started shuttin' the gates to.

So old John turned around and down the stairsteps he went. Got down there on the road to hell, a-staggerin' along with his hands in his pockets a-whistlin'. And when he come in sight of the gates of hell, one of them little devils happened to peek out.

"Daddy! O Daddy! Look a-yonder!"

The old Devil come runnin' and when he saw who it was a-comin', he hollered out, says, "Bar the door, boys! Bar the door!"

Them little devils grabbed the big gates and slammed 'em to quick, turned the key in the lock. So when Wicked John come on up and looked through the bars there stood the old Devil with his young 'uns crowdin' around behind him just a-tremblin'.

"Un-unh!" the old Devil says. "Get on away from here now! No, indeed, you ain't comin' in! I'll not *have* ye! Don't ye come no closter! You just turn around right there now, and put off from here."

Wicked John studied a minute, says, "Well, con-found! I don't know what'n the nation to do now. Saint Peter wouldn't let me in up yonder, and here you've done locked me out. Why, I don't know where to go to!"

So the Devil he looked around, grabbed him up a set of tongs, reached in the furnace, and got holt on a hot coal. Handed it out the bars, says, "Here, old man, you jest take this chunk of fire, and go on off somewhere else, and start you a hell of your own."

Old John he took it; and they tell me that if you go down in the Great Dismal Swamps, you can look out of a night and see a little bob of a light a-movin' along out there. And some folks call it the Jacky-my-lantern, and some call it the will-o'-the-whisp— but I reckon you know now who it is.

There was a lively burst of laughter from all the boys; and one of the three in front of Old Robin flung himself head-over-heels in his laughing fit much to the delight of us all.

"Hit's wrong, tellin' these boys such a pack of foolishness," said Sarah. "Them old tales ought to be left alone anyhow."

"Humpf!" went Granny London. "You listened as hard as the kids did the other day when I told 'em what I remembered about Poll and Betts and Mutsmag."

"Tell it! Tell it!" came from the children.

"Deely here knows it better'n me now. I'm forgetful and liable to leave out part of it. You tell it for 'em, Deely."

Delia looked around, and then let her chin sink thoughtfully. "Well, the way I've always heard it told——"

From *Grandfather Tales*
by Richard Chase

66

THE GLORIOUS WHITEWASHER

SAMUEL L. CLEMENS

Saturday morning was come, and all the summer world was bright and fresh, and brimming with life. There was a song in every heart; and if the heart was young the music issued at the lips. There was cheer in every face and a spring in every step. The locust trees were in bloom and the fragrance of the blossoms filled the air. Cardiff Hill, beyond the village and above it, was green with vegetation, and it lay just far enough away to seem a Delectable Land, dreamy, reposeful, and inviting.

Tom appeared on the sidewalk with a bucket of whitewash and a long-handled brush. He surveyed the fence, and all gladness left him and a deep melancholy settled down upon his spirit. Thirty yards of board fence nine feet high. Life to him seemed hollow, and existence but a burden. Sighing he dipped his brush and passed it along the topmost plank; repeated the operation, did it again; compared the insignificant whitewashed streak with the far-reaching continent of unwhitewashed fence, and sat down on a tree-box discouraged. Jim came skipping out at the gate with a tin pail, and singing "Buffalo Gals." Bringing water from the town pump had always been hateful work in Tom's eyes, before, but now it did not strike him so. He remembered that there was company at the pump. White, mulatto, and negro boys and girls were always there waiting their turns, resting, trading playthings, quarreling, fighting, skylarking. And he remembered that although the pump was only a hundred and fifty yards off, Jim never got back with a bucket of water under an hour—and even then somebody generally had to go after him. Tom said:

"Say, Jim, I'll fetch the water if you'll whitewash some."

Jim shook his head and said:

"Can't, Mars Tom. Ole missis, she tole me I got to go an' git dis water an' not stop foolin' roun' wid anybody. She say she spec' Mars Tom gwine to ax me to whitewash, an' so she tole me go 'long an' 'tend to my own business—she 'lowed *she'd* 'tend to de whitewashin'."

"Oh, never you mind what she said, Jim. That's the way she always talks. Gimme the bucket—I won't be gone only a minute. *She* won't ever know."

"Oh, I dasn't, Mars Tom. Ole missis she'd take an' tar de head off'n me. 'Deed she would."

"*She!* She never licks anybody—whacks 'em over the head with her thimble—and who cares for that, I'd like to know. She talks awful, but talk don't hurt—anyways it don't if she don't cry. Jim, I'll give you a marvel. I'll give you a white alley!"

Jim began to waver.

"White alley, Jim! And it's a bully taw."

"My! Dat's a mighty gay marvel, I tell you! But Mars Tom, I's powerful 'fraid ole missis——"

"And besides, if you will I'll show you my sore toe."

Jim was only human—this attraction was too much for him. He put down his pail, took the white alley, and bent over the toe with absorbing interest while the bandage was being unwound. In another moment he was flying down the street with his pail and a tingling rear, Tom was whitewashing with vigor, and Aunt Polly was retiring from the field with a slipper in her hand and triumph in her eye.

But Tom's energy did not last. He began to think of the fun he had planned for this day, and his sorrows multiplied. Soon the free boys would come tripping along on all sorts of delicious expeditions, and they would make a world of fun of him for having to work—the very thought of it burnt him like fire. He got out his worldly wealth and examined it—bits of toys, marbles, and trash; enough to buy an exchange of *work*, maybe, but not half enough to buy so much as half an hour of pure freedom. So he returned his straitened means to his pocket, and gave up the idea of trying to buy the boys. At this dark and hopeless moment an inspiration burst upon him! Nothing less than a great, magnificent inspiration.

He took up his brush and went tranquilly to work. Ben Rogers hove in sight presently—the very boy, of all boys, whose ridicule he had been dreading. Ben's gait was the hop-skip-and-jump— proof enough that his heart was light and his anticipations high. He was eating an apple, and giving a long, melodious whoop, at intervals, followed by a deep-toned ding-dong-dong, ding-dong-dong, for he was personating a steamboat. As he drew near, he slackened speed, took the middle of the street, leaned far over to starboard and rounded to ponderously and with laborious pomp and circumstance—for he was personating the *Big Missouri*, and considered himself to be drawing nine feet of water. He was boat and captain and engine-bells combined, so he had to imagine himself standing on his own hurricane-deck giving the orders and executing them:

"Stop her, sir! Ting-a-ling-ling!" The headway ran almost out and he drew up slowly toward the sidewalk.

"Ship up to back! Ting-a-ling-ling!" His arms straightened and stiffened down his sides.

"Set her back on the stabboard! Ting-a-ling-ling! Chow! ch-chow-wow! Chow!" His right hand, meantime, describing stately circles—for it was representing a forty-foot wheel.

"Let her go back on the labboard! Ting-a-ling-ling! Chow-ch-chow-chow!" The left hand began to describe circles.

"Stop the stabboard! Ting-a-ling-ling! Stop the labboard! Come ahead on the stabboard! Stop her! Let your outside turn over slow! Ting-a-ling-ling! Chow-ow-ow! Get out that head-line! *Lively* now! Come—out with your spring-line—what're you about there! Take a turn round that stump with the bight of it! Stand by that stage, now—let her go! Done with the engines, sir! Ting-a-ling-ling! *Sh't! s'h't! sh't!*" (trying the gaugecocks).

Tom went on whitewashing—paid no attention to the steamboat. Ben stared a moment and then said:

"Hi-*yi! You're* up a stump, ain't you!"

No answer. Tom surveyed his last touch with the eye of an artist, then he gave his brush another gentle sweep and surveyed the result, as before. Ben ranged up alongside of him. Tom's mouth watered for the apple, but he stuck to his work. Ben said:

"Hello, old chap, you got to work, hey?"

Tom wheeled suddenly and said:

"Why, it's you, Ben! I warn't noticing."

"Say—*I'm* going in a-swimming, *I* am. Don't you wish you could? But of course you'd druther *work*—wouldn't you? Course you would!"

Tom contemplated the boy a bit, and said:

"What do you call work?"

"Why, ain't *that* work?"

Tom resumed his whitewashing, and answered carelessly:

"Well, maybe it is, and maybe it ain't. All I know is, it suits Tom Sawyer."

"Oh come, now, you don't mean to let on that you *like* it?"

The brush continued to move.

"Like it? Well, I don't see why I oughtn't to like it. Does a boy get a chance to whitewash a fence every day?"

That put the thing in a new light. Ben stopped nibbling his apple. Tom swept his brush daintily back and forth—stepped back to note the effect—added a touch here and there—criticized the effect again—Ben watching every move and getting more and more interested, more and more absorbed. Presently he said:

"Say, Tom, let *me* whitewash a little."

Tom considered, was about to consent; but he altered his mind:

"No—no—I reckon it wouldn't hardly do, Ben. You see, Aunt Polly's awful particular about this fence—right here on the street, you know—but if it was the back fence I wouldn't mind and *she* wouldn't. Yes, she's awful particular about this fence; it's got to be done very careful; I reckon there ain't one boy in a thousand, maybe two thousand, that can do it the way it's got to be done."

"No—is that so? Oh come, now—lemme just try. Only just a little—I'd let *you*, if you was me, Tom."

"Ben, I'd like to, honest injun; but Aunt Polly—well, Jim wanted to do it, but she wouldn't let him; Sid wanted to do it, and she wouldn't let Sid. Now don't you see how I'm fixed? If you was to tackle this fence and anything was to happen to it——"

"Oh, shucks, I'll be just as careful. Now lemme try. Say—I'll give you the core of my apple."

"Well, here—No, Ben, now don't. I'm afeard——"

"I'll give you *all* of it!"

Tom gave up the brush with reluctance in his face, but alacrity in his heart. And while the late steamer *Big Missouri* worked and sweated in the sun, the retired artist sat on a barrel in the shade close by, dangled his legs, munched his apple, and planned the slaughter of more innocents. There was no lack of material; boys happened along every little while; they came to jeer, but remained to whitewash. By the time Ben was fagged out, Tom had traded the next chance to Billy Fisher for a kite, in good repair; and when *he* played out, Johnny Miller bought in for a dead rat and a string to swing it with—and so on, and so on, hour after hour. And when the middle of the afternoon came, from being a poor poverty-stricken boy in the morning, Tom was literally rolling in wealth. He had beside the things before mentioned, twelve marbles, part of a jews'-harp, a piece of blue bottle-glass to look through, a spool cannon, a key that wouldn't unlock anything, a fragment of chalk, a glass stopper of a decanter, a tin soldier, a couple of tadpoles, six firecrackers, a kitten with only one eye, a brass door-knob, a dog-collar—but no dog—the handle of a knife, four pieces of orange-peel, and a dilapidated old window-sash.

Tom sat literally rolling in wealth.

He had had a nice, good, idle time all the while—plenty of company—and the fence had three coats of whitewash on it! If he hadn't run out of whitewash, he would have bankrupted every boy in the village.

Tom said to himself that it was not such a hollow world, after all. He had discovered a great law of human action, without knowing it—namely, that in order to make a man or a boy covet a thing, it is only necessary to make the thing difficult to attain. If he had been a great and wise philosopher, like the writer of this book, he would now have comprehended that Work consists of whatever a body is *obliged* to do, and that Play consists of whatever a body is not obliged to do. And this would help him to understand why constructing artificial flowers or performing on a treadmill is work, while rolling tenpins or climbing Mont Blanc is only amusement. There are wealthy gentlemen in England who drive four-horse passenger-coaches twenty or thirty miles on a daily line, in the summer, because the privilege costs them considerable money; but if they were offered wages for the service, that would turn it into work and then they would resign.

The boy mused awhile over the substantial change which had taken place in his worldly circumstances, and then wended toward headquarters to report.

From *Adventures of Tom Sawyer*
by Samuel L. Clemens

THE PETERKINS CELEBRATE
THE FOURTH OF JULY

LUCRETIA P. HALE

THE DAY began early.

A compact had been made with the little boys the evening before.

They were to be allowed to usher in the glorious day by the blowing of horns exactly at sunrise. But they were to blow them for precisely five minutes only, and no sound of the horns should be heard afterward till the family were downstairs.

It was thought that a peace might thus be bought by a short, though crowded, period of noise.

The morning came. Even before the morning, at half-past three o'clock, a terrible blast of the horns aroused the whole family.

Mrs. Peterkin clasped her hands to her head and exclaimed: "I am thankful the lady from Philadelphia is not here!" For she had been invited to stay a week, but had declined to come before the Fourth of July, as she was not well, and her doctor had prescribed quiet.

And the number of the horns was most remarkable! It was as though every cow in the place had arisen and was blowing through both her own horns!

"How many little boys are there? How many have we?" exclaimed Mr. Peterkin, going over their names one by one mechanically, thinking he would do it, as he might count imaginary sheep jumping over a fence, to put himself to sleep. Alas! the counting could not put him to sleep now, in such a din.

And how unexpectedly long the five minutes seemed! Elizabeth Eliza was to take out her watch and give the signal for the end of the five minutes, and the ceasing of the horns. Why did not the signal come? Why did not Elizabeth Eliza stop them?

And certainly it was long before sunrise; there was no dawn to be seen!

"We will not try this plan again," said Mrs. Peterkin.

"If we live to another Fourth," added Mr. Peterkin, hastening to the door to inquire into the state of affairs.

Alas! Amanda, by mistake, had waked up the little boys an hour too early. And by another mistake the little boys had invited three or four of their friends to spend the night with them. Mrs. Peterkin had given them permission to have the boys for the whole day, and they understood the day as beginning when they went to bed the night before. This accounted for the number of horns.

It would have been impossible to hear any explanation; but the five minutes were over, and the horns had ceased, and there remained only the noise of a singular leaping of feet, explained perhaps by a possible pillow-fight, that kept the family below partially awake until the bells and cannon made known the dawning of the glorious day,—the sunrise, or "the rising of the sons," as Mr. Peterkin jocosely called it when they heard the little boys and their friends clattering down the stairs to begin the outside festivities.

They were bound first for the swamp, for Elizabeth Eliza, at the suggestion of the lady from Philadelphia, had advised them to hang some flags around the pillars of the piazza. Now the little boys knew of a place in the swamp where they had been in the habit of digging for "flag-root," and where they might find plenty of flag flowers. They did bring away all they could, but they were a little out of bloom. The boys were in the midst of nailing up all they had on the pillars of the piazza, when the procession of the Antiques and Horribles passed along. As the procession saw the festive arrangements on the piazza, and the crowd of boys, who cheered them loudly, it stopped to salute the house with some especial strains of greeting.

Poor Mrs. Peterkin! They were directly under her windows! In a few moments of quiet, during the boys' absence from the house on their visit to the swamp, she had been trying to find out whether she had a sick-headache, or whether it was all the noise, and she was just deciding it was the sick headache, but was falling into a light slumber, when the fresh noise outside began.

There were the imitations of the crowing of cocks, and braying of donkeys, and the sound of horns, encored and increased by the cheers of the boys. Then began the torpedoes, and the Antiques and Horribles had Chinese crackers also.

And, in despair of sleep, the family came down to breakfast.

Mrs. Peterkin had always been much afraid of fireworks, and

had never allowed the boys to bring gunpowder into the house. She was even afraid of torpedoes; they looked so much like sugar-plums she was sure some of the children would swallow them, and explode before anybody knew it.

She was very timid about other things. She was not sure even about pea-nuts. Everybody exclaimed over this: "Surely there was no danger in pea-nuts!" But Mrs. Peterkin declared she had been very much alarmed at the Centennial Exhibition, and in the crowded corners of the streets in Boston, at the pea-nut stands, where they had machines to roast the pea-nuts. She did not think it was safe. They might go off any time, in the midst of a crowd of people, too!

Mr. Peterkin thought there actually was no danger, and he should be sorry to give up the pea-nut. He thought it an American institution, something really belonging to the Fourth of July. He even confessed to a quiet pleasure in crushing the empty shells with his feet on the sidewalks as he went along the streets.

Agamemnon thought it a simple joy.

In consideration, however, of the fact that they had had no real celebration of the Fourth the last year, Mrs. Peterkin had con-sented to give over the day, this year, to the amusement of the family as a Centennial celebration. She would prepare herself for a terrible noise,—only she did not want any gunpowder brought into the house.

The little boys had begun by firing some torpedoes a few days beforehand, that their mother might be used to the sound, and had selected their horns some weeks before.

Solomon John had been very busy in inventing some fireworks. As Mrs. Peterkin objected to the use of gunpowder, he found out from the dictionary what the different parts of gunpowder are,—

saltpetre, charcoal, and sulphur. Charcoal, he discovered, they had in the wood-house; saltpetre they would find in the cellar, in the beef barrel; and sulphur they could buy at the apothecary's. He explained to his mother that these materials had never yet exploded in the house, and she was quieted.

Agamemnon, meanwhile, remembered a recipe he had read somewhere for making a "fulminating paste" of iron-filings and powder of brimstone. He had written it down on a piece of paper in his pocket-book. But the iron filings must be finely powdered. This they began upon a day or two before, and the very afternoon before laid out some of the paste on the piazza.

Pin-wheels and rockets were contributed by Mr. Peterkin for the evening. According to a programme drawn up by Agamemnon and Solomon John, the reading of the Declaration of Independence was to take place in the morning, on the piazza, under the flags.

The Bromwicks brought over their flag to hang over the door.

"That is what the lady from Philadelphia meant," explained Elizabeth Eliza.

"She said the flags of our country," said the little boys. "We thought she meant 'in the country.'"

Quite a company assembled; but it seemed nobody had a copy of the Declaration of Independence.

Elizabeth Eliza said she could say one line, if they each could add as much. But it proved they all knew the same line that she did, as they began:—

"When, in the course of—when, in the course of—when, in the course of human—when in the course of human events—when, in the course of human events, it becomes—when, in the course of human events, it becomes necessary—when, in the course of human events, it becomes necessary for one people"—

They could not get any farther. Some of the party decided that "one people" was a good place to stop, and the little boys sent off some fresh torpedoes in honor of the people. But Mr. Peterkin was not satisfied. He invited the assembled party to stay until sunset, and meanwhile he would find a copy, and torpedoes were to be saved to be fired off at the close of every sentence.

And now the noon bells rang and the noon bells ceased.

Mrs. Peterkin wanted to ask everybody to dinner. She should have some cold beef. She had let Amanda go, because it was the Fourth, and everybody ought to be free that one day; so she could not have much of a dinner. But when she went to cut her beef she found Solomon had taken it to soak, on account of the saltpetre, for the fireworks!

Well, they had a pig; so she took a ham, and the boys had bought tamarinds and buns and a cocoa-nut. So the company stayed on, and when the Antiques and Horribles passed again they were treated to pea-nuts and lemonade.

They sung patriotic songs, they told stories, they fired torpedoes, they frightened the cats with them. It was a warm afternoon; the red poppies were out wide, and the hot sun poured down on the alley-ways in the garden. There was a seething sound of a hot day in the buzzing of insects, in the steaming heat that came up from the ground. Some neighboring boys were firing a toy cannon. Every time it went off Mrs. Peterkin started, and looked to see if one of the little boys was gone. Mr. Peterkin had set out to find a copy of the "Declaration." Agamemnon had disappeared. She had not a moment to decide about her headache. She asked Ann Maria if she were not anxious about the fireworks, and if rockets were not dangerous. They went up, but you were never sure where they came down.

And then came a fresh tumult! All the fire-engines in town

rushed toward them, clanging with bells, men and boys yelling! They were out for a practice, and for a Fourth-of-July show.

Mrs. Peterkin thought the house was on fire, and so did some of the guests. There was great rushing hither and thither. Some thought they would better go home; some thought they would better stay. Mrs. Peterkin hastened into the house to save herself, or see what she could save. Elizabeth Eliza followed her, first proceeding to collect all the pokers and tongs she could find, because they could be thrown out of the window without breaking. She had read of people who had flung looking-glasses out of the window by mistake, in the excitement of the house being on fire, and had carried the pokers and tongs carefully into the garden. There was nothing like being prepared. She had always determined to do the reverse. So with calmness she told Solomon John to take down the looking-glasses. But she met with a difficulty,—there were no pokers and tongs, as they did not use them. They had no open fires; Mrs. Peterkin had been afraid of them. So Elizabeth Eliza took all the pots and kettles up to the upper windows, ready to be thrown out.

But where was Mrs. Peterkin? Solomon John found she had fled to the attic in terror. He persuaded her to come down, assuring her it was the most unsafe place; but she insisted upon stopping to collect some bags of old pieces, that nobody would think of saving from the general wreck, she said, unless she did. Alas! this was the result of fireworks on Fourth of July! As they came downstairs they heard the voices of all the company declaring there was no fire; the danger was past. It was long before Mrs. Peterkin could believe it. They told her the fire company was only out for show, and to celebrate the Fourth of July. She thought it already too much celebrated.

Elizabeth Eliza's kettles and pans had come down through the windows with a crash, that had only added to the festivities, the little boys thought.

Mr. Peterkin had been roaming about all this time in search of a copy of the Declaration of Independence. The public library was shut, and he had to go from house to house; but now, as the sunset bells and cannon began, he returned with a copy, and read it, to the pealing of the bells and sounding of the cannon. Torpedoes and crackers were fired at every pause. Some sweet-marjoram pots, tin cans filled with crackers which were lighted, went off with great explosions.

At the most exciting moment, near the close of the reading, Agamemnon, with an expression of terror, pulled Solomon John aside.

"I have suddenly remembered where I read about the 'fulminating paste' we made. It was in the preface to 'Woodstock,' and I have been round to borrow the book, to read the directions over again, because I was afraid about the 'paste' going off. READ THIS QUICKLY! and tell me, *Where is the fulminating paste?*"

Solomon John was busy winding some covers of paper over a little parcel. It contained chlorate of potash and sulphur mixed. A friend had told him of the composition. The more thicknesses of paper you put round it the louder it would go off. You must pound it with a hammer. Solomon John felt it must be perfectly safe, as his mother had taken potash for a medicine.

He still held the parcel as he read from Agamemnon's book: "This paste, when it has lain together about twenty-six hours, will *of itself* take fire, and burn all the sulphur away with a blue flame and a bad smell."

"Where is the paste?" repeated Solomon John, in terror.

"We made it just twenty-six hours ago," said Agamemnon.

"We put it on the piazza," exclaimed Solomon John, rapidly recalling the facts, "and it is in front of our mother's feet!"

He hastened to snatch the paste away before it should take fire, flinging aside the packet in his hurry. Agamemnon, jumping upon the piazza at the same moment, trod upon the paper parcel, which exploded at once with the shock, and he fell to the ground, while at the same moment the paste "fulminated" into a blue flame directly in front of Mrs. Peterkin!

It was a moment of great confusion. There were cries and screams. The bells were still ringing, the cannon firing, and Mr. Peterkin had just reached the closing words: "Our lives, our fortunes, and our sacred honor."

"We are all blown up, as I feared we should be," Mrs. Peterkin at length ventured to say, finding herself in a lilac-bush by the side of the piazza. She scarcely dared to open her eyes to see the scattered limbs about her.

It was so with all. Even Ann Maria Bromwick clutched a pillar of the piazza, with closed eyes.

At length Mr. Peterkin said, calmly, "Is anybody killed?"

There was no reply. Nobody could tell whether it was because everybody was killed, or because they were too wounded to answer. It was a great while before Mrs. Peterkin ventured to move.

But the little boys soon shouted with joy, and cheered the success of Solomon John's fireworks, and hoped he had some more. One of them had his face blackened by an unexpected cracker, and Elizabeth Eliza's muslin dress was burned here and there. But no one was hurt; no one had lost any limbs, though Mrs. Peterkin was sure she had seen some flying in the air. Nobody could understand how, as she had kept her eyes firmly shut.

Agamemnon fell to the ground.

No greater accident had occurred than the singeing of the tip of Solomon John's nose. But there was an unpleasant and terrible odor from the "fulminating paste."

Mrs. Peterkin was extricated from the lilac-bush. No one knew how she got there. Indeed, the thundering noise had stunned everybody. It had roused the neighborhood even more than before. Answering explosions came on every side, and, though the sunset light had not faded away, the little boys hastened to send off rockets under cover of the confusion. Solomon John's other fire-works would not go. But all felt he had done enough.

Mrs. Peterkin retreated into the parlor, deciding she really did have a headache. At times she had to come out when a rocket went off, to see if it was one of the little boys. She was exhausted by the adventures of the day, and almost thought it could not have been worse if the boys had been allowed gunpowder. The distracted lady was thankful there was likely to be but one Centennial Fourth in her lifetime, and declared she should never more keep anything in the house as dangerous as saltpetred beef, and she should never venture to take another spoonful of potash.

From *The Peterkin Papers*
by Lucretia P. Hale

THE BREMEN TOWN-MUSICIANS

THE BROTHERS GRIMM

ACERTAIN man had a donkey, which had carried the corn-sacks to the mill indefatigably for many a long year; but his strength was going, and he was growing more and more unfit for work. Then his master began to consider how he might best save his keep; but the donkey, seeing that no good wind was blowing, ran away and set out on the road to Bremen. "There," he thought, "I can surely be town-musician." When he had walked some distance, he found a hound lying on the road, gasping like one who had run till he was tired. "What are you gasping so for, you big fellow?" asked the donkey.

"Ah," replied the hound, "as I am old, and daily grow weaker, and no longer can hunt, my master wanted to kill me, so I took to flight; but now how am I to earn my bread?"

"I tell you what," said the donkey, "I am going to Bremen, and shall be town-musician there; go with me and engage yourself also as a musician. I will play the lute, and you shall beat the kettle-drum."

The hound agreed, and on they went.

Before long they came to a cat, sitting on the path, with a face like three rainy days! "Now then, old shaver, what has gone askew with you?" asked the donkey.

"Who can be merry when his neck is in danger?" answered the cat. "Because I am now getting old, and my teeth are worn to stumps, and I prefer to sit by the fire and spin, rather than hunt about after mice, my mistress wanted to drown me, so I ran away. But now good advice is scarce. Where am I to go?"

"Go with us to Bremen. You understand night-music, so you can be a town-musician."

The cat thought well of it, and went with them. After this the three fugitives came to a farm-yard, where the cock was sitting upon the gate, crowing with all his might. "Your crow goes through and through one," said the donkey. "What is the matter?"

"I have been foretelling fine weather, because it is the day on which Our Lady washes the Christ-child's little shirts, and wants to dry them," said the cock; "but guests are coming for Sunday, so the housewife has no pity, and has told the cook that she intends to eat me in the soup to-morrow, and this evening I am to have my head cut off. Now I am crowing at the top of my lungs while still I can."

"Ah, but red-comb," said the donkey, "you had better come away with us. We are going to Bremen; you can find something better than death everywhere: you have a good voice, and if we make music together it must have some quality!"

The cock agreed to this plan, and all four went on together. They could not reach the city of Bremen in one day, however, and in the evening they came to a forest where they meant to pass the night. The donkey and the hound laid themselves down under a large tree, the cat and the cock settled themselves in the branches; but the cock flew right to the top, where he was most safe. Before he went to sleep he looked round on all four sides, and thought he saw in the distance a little spark burning; so he called out to his companions that there must be a house not far off, for he saw a light. The donkey said: "If so, we had better get up and go on, for the shelter here is bad." The hound thought too that a few bones with some meat on would do him good!

So they made their way to the place where the light was, and soon saw it shine brighter and grow larger, until they came to a well-lighted robbers' house. The donkey, as the biggest, went to the window and looked in.

"What do you see, my grey-horse?" asked the cock. "What do I see?" answered the donkey; "a table covered with good things to eat and drink, and robbers sitting at it enjoying themselves." "That would be the sort of thing for us," said the cock. "Yes, yes; ah, if only we were there!" said the donkey.

Then the animals took counsel together how they should manage to drive away the robbers, and at last they thought of a plan. The donkey was to place himself with his fore-feet upon the window-ledge, the hound was to jump on the donkey's back, the cat was to climb upon the dog, and lastly the cock was to fly up and perch upon the head of the cat.

When this was done, at a given signal, they began to perform their music together: the donkey brayed, the hound barked, the cat mewed, and the cock crowed; then they burst through the window into the room, shattering the glass! At this horrible din, the robbers sprang up, thinking no otherwise than that a ghost had

The donkey, as the biggest, went to the window and looked in.

come in, and fled in a great fright out into the forest. The four companions now sat down at the table, well content with what was left, and ate as if they were going to fast for a month.

As soon as the four minstrels had done, they put out the light, and each sought for himself a sleeping-place according to his nature and to what suited him. The donkey laid himself down upon some straw in the yard, the hound behind the door, the cat upon the hearth near the warm ashes, and the cock perched himself upon a beam of the roof; and being tired from their long walk, they soon went to sleep.

When it was past midnight, and the robbers saw from afar that the light was no longer burning in their house, and all appeared quiet, the captain said: "We ought not to have let ourselves be frightened out of our wits"; and ordered one of them to go and examine the house.

The messenger finding all still, went into the kitchen to light a candle, and, taking the glistening fiery eyes of the cat for live coals, he held a lucifer-match to them to light it. But the cat did not understand the joke, and flew in his face, spitting and scratching. He was dreadfully frightened, and ran to the back-door, but the dog, who lay there, sprang up and bit his leg; and as he ran across the yard by the dunghill, the donkey gave him a smart kick with its hind foot. The cock, too, who had been awakened by the noise, and had become lively, cried down from the beam: "Cock-a-doodle-doo!"

Then the robber ran back as fast as he could to his captain, and said: "Ah, there is a horrible witch sitting in the house, who spat on me and scratched my face with her long claws; and by the door stands a man with a knife, who stabbed me in the leg; and in the yard there lies a black monster, who beat me with a wooden club;

and above, upon the roof, sits the judge, who called out, 'Bring the rogue here to me!' so I got away as well as I could."

After this the robbers never again dared enter the house; but it suited the four musicians of Bremen so well that they did not care to leave it any more. And the mouth of him who last told this story is still warm.

From *Grimm's Fairy Tales*

THE LITTLE DRESSMAKER

ELEANOR FARJEON

THERE was once a Little Dressmaker who was apprentice to a Big Dressmaker. But although she was only an apprentice she cut her patterns so beautifully, and took her stitches so daintily, and had such charming fancies about the frocks she made, that she was really the best dressmaker in the kingdom, and the Big Dressmaker knew it. But the Little Dressmaker was so young and so modest, that the Big Dressmaker said to herself:

'There is no need to tell Lotta she is a better dressmaker than I am. If I don't tell her, she will never find out for herself, and if I do tell her she will go away and set up a Rival Establishment.'

So the Big Dressmaker held her tongue, and did not always praise Lotta when she had done something prettier than usual, and quite often scolded her when she had done nothing whatever to deserve it. But Lotta took it all in good part; and she did not suspect her own worth, even when the Big Dressmaker came to her for advice, as, when she had a particularly important order, she always did.

'The Marchioness of Roley-Poley has just been in to order a ball dress, Lotta,' the Big Dressmaker would say. 'She fancies herself in peach-coloured silk.'

'Oh, what a pity!' Lotta would cry. 'She would look so much better in plum-coloured velvet.'

'Exactly what I told her,' said the Big Dressmaker. 'She wants seventeen flounces on the skirt.'

'Fancy that!' exclaimed Lotta. 'She ought to have it as plain as plain but with a dignified cut.'

'Precisely,' said the Big Dressmaker. 'As I said to the Marchioness with my very own lips, a dignified cut is the thing, and as plain as plain can be.'

So instead of making the Marchioness of Roley-Poley a flouncy peach-coloured dress, they made her a dignified plum-coloured one; and the Marchioness looked extremely imposing at the Queen's reception, and everybody said, 'The Big Dressmaker is a genius.'

But it was really little Lotta.

Now you must know that the Queen of the country was seventy years old and, being unmarried, had no children to succeed to the throne. But if she had never been a mother, she had at least been, for twenty-five years, an aunt; and her nephew, who was King of the kingdom next door, would in the course of time rule over her country as well as his own. He hadn't visited his aunt for twenty years, but report said he was a charming young man, and, like his aunt, he was unmarried—a circumstance which bothered her so much that she wrote to him about it twice a year: at Christmas and on his birthday. But he always wrote back:

'Dear Aunt Georgey,
                    Thank you awfully for the jolly pencil-case.
                         Your loving Nephew,
                                    Dick.
P.S. There's plenty of time.'

But old Georgina was seventy and young King Richard was twenty-five, and at seventy there does not seem to be quite so much time as there does at twenty-five; so presently the Queen, who was a masterful old lady, wrote a letter in between Christmas and his birthday, to tell him he must come to her Court and choose for himself a bride from among the Court ladies, because she was sick and tired of his stuff and nonsense. As this time she hadn't sent him a pencil-case, the King couldn't put her off with thanks, and the chief part of his letter had to be about the marriage. So he wrote:

'Dear Aunt Georgey,
                    Just as you like.
                         Your loving Nephew,
                                    Dick.
P.S. I won't marry anybody who isn't nineteen-and-a-half years old, and nineteen-and-a-half inches round the waist.'

The Queen immediately summoned all the Court ladies of nineteen-and-a-half years old, and had them measured. There were exactly three whose waists were nineteen-and-a-half inches, no more and no less. So she wrote again to her nephew.

'My dear Richard,
                    The Duchess of Junkets, the Countess of Caramel, and the Lady Blanche Blancmange will all be twenty next December; the present month being

June. They are delightful girls, and their waists meet your requirements. Come and choose for yourself.

Your affectionate Aunt,

Georgina Regina.'

To this the King replied:

'Dear Aunt Georgey,

Have it your own way. I'll come on Monday. Please give three balls, on Tuesday, Wednesday, and Thursday, and let me have each of the ladies in turn for my partner. I'll marry the one I like best on Friday, and go home on Saturday.

Your loving Nephew,

Dick.

P.S. I'd like the balls to be fancy dress, because I've got an awfully good one.'

The Queen did not get this letter till Monday morning, and the King was coming that very night. You can imagine what a flutter everybody was in, particularly the ladies with the nineteen-and-a-half-inch waists! Of course, they paid a visit to the Big Dressmaker at once.

Said the Duchess of Junkets:

'I positively *must* have the most beautiful fancy dress you can make me, and that on Tuesday in time for the First Ball. And be sure, when it is ready, you send me one of your girls to show me how to wear it.'

Said the Countess of Caramel:

'It is of the utmost importance that you should make me the most fascinating fancy dress you can think of, and deliver it on Wednesday in time for the Second Ball. And let your best apprentice bring it, to set it off for me.'

Said the Lady Blanche Blancmange:

'I shall expire of vexation if you do not create for me the most enchanting fancy dress in the world, to be worn on Thursday night at the Third Ball. And that I may see it is quite perfect, put it on your daintiest model so that I can judge the effect for myself.'

The Big Dressmaker promised them all, and as soon as the ladies had departed she rushed in to Lotta and told her all about it.

'We must think with all our brains, and sew with all our fingers, Lotta, if we are to get them done in time!'

'Oh, I'm sure I can manage,' said Lotta cheerfully. 'We'll take the dresses in order, and the Duchess shall have hers tomorrow night, and the Countess shall have hers the next night, and the Lady Blanche shall have hers the night after that, if I have to sit up all the time and never go to bed at all.'

'Very well, Lotta,' said the Big Dressmaker. 'But now I must consider what the dresses will be.'

'The Duchess would look beautiful as a Sunbeam,' said Lotta.

'Just what *I* was thinking,' said the Big Dressmaker.

'And how entrancing the Countess would look as Moonlight,' said Lotta.

'My idea exactly,' said the Big Dressmaker.

'And as a Rainbow the Lady Blanche would look simply ravishing.'

'You have taken the very words out of my mouth,' said the Big Dressmaker. 'Now to design them, cut them out, and make them.'

So Lotta designed the three dresses, and set about making the first one, a radiant golden gown that would flash and sparkle like light as the wearer of it danced. She sat at it day and night, and saw nothing of the young King's arrival at the palace; and on the Tuesday, an hour before the opening of the First Ball, the bright frock was ready.

'They have sent a coach from the palace to fetch it,' said the Big Dressmaker, 'and one of my girls is to wear it and show it off to the Duchess before she puts it on. But whom can I possibly send? It has only a nineteen-and-a-half-inch waist.'

'That's just my size, madam,' said Lotta.

'How fortunate! Quick, Lotta, slip it on and be off.'

So Lotta slipped on the dazzling frock, the golden shoes and slippers, and the little gold crown twinkling with points of light, and throwing her old black cloak over all ran down to the royal coach that was waiting for her. The coachman flicked his whip and away they went. When she arrived at the palace, a Footman who was passing through the hall conducted Lotta to a little anteroom.

'You are to wait here,' said he, 'till the Duchess is ready for you in the next room. When she is, she will ring a bell. What a charming dress you seem to be wearing under your cloak.'

'It is the Duchess's dress,' said Lotta, 'with which she is to captivate the young King. Would you like to see it?'

'Very much indeed,' said the Footman.

Lotta dropped her black cloak, and stepped like a sunbeam out of a cloud.

'There!' she said. 'Isn't it beautiful! Do you think the King will be able to resist dancing with the Duchess in this frock?'

'I am sure he won't,' said the Footman. And making an elegant bow, he added, 'Duchess, may I have the honour of this dance?'

'Oh, Your Majesty!' laughed Lotta. 'The honour is mine.'

The Footman put his arm round Lotta's waist, and danced with her, and just as he was telling her that her hair was more golden than sunlight itself, the bell rang and Lotta had to go.

The Duchess was delighted with the dress, and when Lotta had

*Making an elegant bow, he added, 'Duchess,
may I have the honour of this dance?'*

shown her exactly how to move and sit and stand and dance in it, she put it on and sailed into the ballroom.

Lotta, wrapping herself in her old cloak, heard how everybody broke into applause as the radiant little Duchess appeared.

'Ah,' thought Lotta, 'the King will never be able to resist *her!*' And back she ran, to begin the Moonlight dress.

All night and all day she sewed the slim silver sheath, and she got it done by the following evening, just as the royal coach drew up at the door to fetch her. As before, she slipped on the frock, covered herself with her cloak, and drove away; and as before, the young Footman escorted her to the anteroom and told her to wait.

'And what happened at the ball last night?' asked Lotta.

'The King danced with the Golden Duchess all the evening,' said the Footman. 'I doubt if the Countess will have such luck.'

'Don't you think so?' said Lotta; and opening her black cloak, she stood before him like the moon shining at midnight.

'Oh, Countess!' said the Footman, taking her hand and kissing it, 'will you make me the happiest man in the world by dancing with me?'

'The happiness is mine, Your Majesty,' said Lotta, smiling sweetly.

So once more they danced together in the anteroom, and then they sat down and talked all about themselves and each other; and Lotta told him that she was nineteen-and-a-half years old, and that her mother was a housemaid and her father a cobbler, and she herself an apprentice dressmaker. And the Footman told her that he was twenty-five years old, and that his father was a bookbinder and his mother a laundress, and he himself a footman to the young King, to whose kingdom he would return when the King was married. And this made Lotta thoughtful, and the Footman asked why, and Lotta didn't know. And the Footman took her hand in his, and was just telling her that it was as white as moonlight when the bell rang and Lotta had to go.

The Countess of Caramel was charmed with the frock, and when all its points had been shown off she put it on and entered the ballroom. And Lotta heard the shout of admiration that went up as she appeared; while Lotta herself hurried back in her old cloak to make the Rainbow dress.

All night and all day she sat at it, and her eyes were rather heavy, and her heart was a little heavy too, but she couldn't think why. And just an hour before the Third Ball was to begin, the frock was done and the coach was waiting. Once more Lotta put on a shimmering frock, hid herself in her old cloak, and was driven to the palace. And once more the Footman escorted her to the anteroom, where she sank into a deep chair while he stood before her. And once more Lotta asked, 'What happened at the ball last night?'

'The King danced every dance with the Silver Countess, and never took his eyes off her,' said the Footman. 'I don't suppose there's much chance for the Lady Blanche.'

'You never know,' said Lotta. But she was feeling so tired that she didn't even try to undo her cloak and show him. So the Footman undid it for her, and laid it back against the chair; and when he saw Lotta shining like a little rainbow against a black cloud-bank, he fell on his knees before her.

'Oh, Lady!' he whispered, 'won't you dance this dance with me, and every other dance as well?'

But Lotta shook her head, because she was so tired, and she tried to smile, but at the same time big tears trickled down her cheeks. And the Footman didn't even ask why, since tears seem natural in a rainbow, but he put his arms round her as she sat in the chair and gave her a kiss. And before the kiss was quite finished, the bell rang, and Lotta had to wipe her eyes and go.

The Lady Blanche was ravished with the frock, and after Lotta had turned this way and that way to show her how to wear it, she put it on and ran into the ballroom. Lotta heard a great sigh of wonder go round at the lovely little vision that had appeared. Then she went back to the empty anteroom, put on her old cloak, and stumbled back. She meant to go to bed and sleep and sleep.

But at the door the Big Dressmaker met her with a face of despair.

'What do you think?' cried she. 'An order has just come from the Queen that we must make the finest wedding-dress ever made, for the King's Bride tomorrow. The wedding is to be at noon. Now, think, Lotta, think! What shall the wedding-dress be?'

Lotta thought of a dress as pure as a fall of snow, and as she began to cut it out she said, 'But, madam, we do not know whom it is to fit.'

'Make it to fit yourself,' said the Big Dressmaker. 'For you and the three ladies are all of a size.'

'And which do you think it will be?' asked Lotta.

'Nobody knows. They say the King was equally charmed by the Sun and the Moon, and doubtless he will be by the Rainbow as well.'

'And what dress did the King wear at the ball, madam?' asked Lotta, to keep herself awake.

'A most disappointing dress for a King,' said the Big Dressmaker. 'He wore the livery of his own Footman!'

After that, Lotta asked no more questions. She just bent her tired little head over the pure white stuff, and sewed and sewed till her fingers and her eyes ached.

The night passed, morning came, and an hour before noon the frock was ready.

'The coach is here,' said the Big Dressmaker. 'Put on the dress, Lotta, for the Bride will certainly wish to see how it should be worn.'

'Who *is* the Bride?' asked Lotta.

'Still nobody knows,' said the Big Dressmaker. 'They say the young King is making his choice at this moment, and the wedding will take place as soon as he has decided.'

So Lotta put on the wedding-dress, and went down to the coach, and there, to her surprise, was her own Footman, waiting to hand her in. She looked at him earnestly and said, 'But aren't you the King?' and the Footman said 'Whatever made you think that?' and shut the door, and away they galloped. And Lotta leaned back in a corner, and fell fast asleep, and dreamed she was driving to her wedding.

When she woke up, the coach was just pulling up at a door; but instead of being the palace door, it was the door of a little church in the country.

The Footman jumped down and handed Lotta out; it all seemed a natural part of her dream as she went on his arm up the aisle in her snow-white gown, and found the clergyman waiting at the altar. In two minutes they were married, and Lotta, with a gold ring on her finger, went back to the coach. But this time the Footman got inside with her, and as they drove off he finished giving her the kiss he had begun the night before, and Lotta went to sleep with her head on his shoulder.

She never woke up till they reached the young King's city and stopped before the young King's palace. And there, all in a daze, she found herself going up the steps on the Footman's arm amid the cheers of the populace, and at the top of the steps, waiting to receive them, with a merry smile on his face—*the young King himself.*

Yes; because, you see, the Footman really *was* the Footman. Only, as the young King didn't want to be married a bit, he had sent his Footman in his place. And as the Footman fell in love with Lotta at first sight, he had made up his mind before the very first ball, and after that there wasn't a ghost of a chance for the Duchess of Junkets, the Countess of Caramel, or the Lady Blanche Blancmange. And this was really very fortunate, because if the Footman had chosen and married one of them, the old Queen would have been greatly annoyed when she found out the trick that had been played upon her by her nephew; and the Bride would have been annoyed as well.

As it was, when the facts came to the Queen's ears, she wrote to the young King on his birthday:

'My dear Richard,

I send you the enclosed, with my love. At the same time, I wish to say that I am extremely displeased with you, and shall take no further interest in your matrimonial affairs.

Your affectionate Aunt,

Georgina Regina.'

To which the young King replied:

'Dear Aunt Georgey,

Thanks awfully.

Your loving Nephew,

Dick.

P.S. Oh, and thank you for the jolly pencil-case.'

From *The Little Bookroom*
by Eleanor Farjeon

104

OUR FIELD

JULIANA H. EWING

THERE were four of us, and three of us had godfathers and godmothers. Three each. Three times three make nine, and not a fairy godmother in the lot. That was what vexed us.

It was very provoking, because we knew so well what we wanted if we had one and she had given us three wishes each. Three times three make nine. We could have got all we wanted out of nine wishes, and have provided for Perronet into the bargain. It would not have been any good Perronet having wishes all to himself, because he was only a dog.

We never knew who it was that drowned Perronet, but it was Sandy who saved his life and brought him home. It was when he was coming home from school, and he brought Perronet with him.

Perronet was not at all nice to look at when we first saw him, though we were sorry for him. He was wet all over, and his eyes shut, and you could see his ribs, and he looked quite dark and sticky. But when he dried, he dried a lovely yellow, with two black ears like velvet. People sometimes asked us what kind of dog he was, but we never knew, except that he was the nicest possible kind.

When we had got him, we were afraid we were not going to be allowed to have him. Mother said we could not afford him, because of the tax and his keep. The tax was five shillings, but there wanted nearly a year to the time of paying it. Of course his keep began as soon as he could eat, and that was the very same evening. We were all very miserable, because we were so fond of Perronet—at least, Perronet was not his name then, but he was the same person—and at last it was settled that all three of us would give up sugar, towards saving the expense of his keep, if he might stay. It was hardest for Sandy, because he was particularly fond of sweet things; but then he was particularly fond of Perronet. So we all gave up sugar and Perronet was allowed to remain.

About the tax, we thought we could save any pennies or half-pennies we got during the year, and it was such a long time to the time for paying, that we should be almost sure to have enough by then. We had not any money at the time, or we should have bought a savings-box; but lots of people save their money in stockings, and we settled that we would. An old stocking would not do, because of the holes, and I had not many good pairs; but we took one of my winter ones to use in the summer, and then we thought we could pour the money into one of my good summer ones when the winter came.

What we most of all wanted a fairy godmother for was about

our 'homes.' There was no kind of game we liked better than playing at houses and new homes. But no matter where we made our 'home,' it was sure to be disturbed. If it was indoors, and we made a palace under the big table, as soon as ever we had got it nicely divided into rooms according to where the legs came, it was certain to be dinner-time, and people put their feet into it. The nicest house we ever had was in the outhouse; we had it, and kept it quite a secret, for weeks. And then the new load of wood came and covered up everything, our best oyster-shell dinner service and all.

Anyone can see that it is impossible really to fancy anything when you are constantly interrupted. You can't have any fun out of a railway train stopping at stations, when they take all your carriages to pieces because the chairs are wanted for tea; any more than you can play properly at Grace Darling in a lifeboat, when they say the old cradle is too good to be knocked about in that way.

It was always the same. If we wanted to play at Thames Tunnel under the beds, we were not allowed; and the day we did Aladdin in the store-closet, old Jane came and would put away the soap, just when Aladdin could not possibly have got the door of the cave open.

It was one day early in May—a very hot day for the time of year, which had made us rather cross—when Sandy came in about four o'clock, smiling more broadly even than usual, and said to Richard and me: 'I've got a fairy godmother, and she's given us a field.'

Sandy was very fond of eating, especially sweet things. He used to keep back things from meals to enjoy afterwards, and he almost always had a piece of cake in his pocket. He brought a piece out now, and took a large mouthful, laughing at us with his eyes over the top of it.

'What's the good of a field?' said Richard.

'Splendid houses in it,' said Sandy.

'I'm quite tired of fancying homes,' said I. 'It's no good; we always get turned out.'

'It's quite a new place,' Sandy continued; 'you've never been there,' and he took a triumphant bite of the cake.

'How did you get there?' asked Richard.

'The fairy godmother showed me,' was Sandy's reply.

There is such a thing as nursery honour. We respected each other's pretending unless we were very cross, but I didn't disbelieve in his fairy godmother. I only said: 'You shouldn't talk with your mouth full,' to snub him for making a secret about his field.

Sandy is very good tempered. He only laughed and said: 'Come along. It's much cooler out now. The sun's going down.'

He took us along Gipsy Lane. We had been there once or twice, for walks, but not very often, for there was some horrid story about it which rather frightened us. I do not know what it was, but it was a horrid one. Still we had been there, and I knew it quite well. At the end of it there is a stile, by which you go into a field, and at the other end you get over another stile, and find yourself in the high road.

'If this is our field, Sandy,' said I, when we got to the first stile, 'I'm very sorry, but it really won't do. I know that lots of people come through it. We should never be quiet here.'

Sandy laughed. He didn't speak, and he didn't get over the stile; he went through a gate close by it leading into a little sort of by-lane that was all mud in winter and hard cart-ruts in summer. I had never been up it, but I had seen hay and that sort of thing go in and come out of it.

He went on and we followed him. The ruts were very disagreeable to walk on, but presently he led us through a hole in the hedge, and we got into a field. It was a very bare-looking field, and went rather uphill. There was no path, but Sandy walked away up it, and we went after him. There was another hedge at the top, and a stile in it. It had very rough posts, one much longer than the other, and the cross step was gone, but there were two rails, and we all climbed over. And when we got to the other side, Sandy leaned against the big post and gave a wave with his right hand and said: 'This is our field.'

It sloped downhill, and the hedges round it were rather high, with awkward branches of blackthorn sticking out here and there without any leaves, and with the blossom lying white on the black twigs like snow. There were cowslips all over the field, but they were thicker at the lower end, which was damp. The great heat of the day was over. The sun shone still, but it shone low down and made such splendid shadows that we all walked about with grey giants at our feet; and it made the bright green of the grass, and the cowslips down below, and the top of the hedge, and Sandy's hair, and everything in the sun and the mist behind the elder bush which was out of the sun, so yellow—so very yellow—that just for a minute I really believed about Sandy's godmother, and thought it was a story come true, and that everything was turning into gold.

But it was only for a minute; of course I know that fairy-tales are not true. But it was a lovely field, and when we had put our hands to our eyes and had a good look at it, I said to Sandy: 'I beg your pardon, Sandy, for telling you not to talk with your mouth full. It is the best field I ever heard of.'

'Sit down,' said Sandy, doing the honours; and we all sat down under the hedge.

'There are violets just behind us,' he continued. 'Can't you smell them? But whatever you do don't tell anybody about them, or we shan't keep our field to ourselves for a day. And look here,' He had turned over on to his face, and Richard and I did the same, whilst Sandy fumbled among the bleached grass and brown leaves.

'Hyacinths,' said Richard, as Sandy displayed the green tops of them.

'As thick as peas,' said Sandy. 'This bank will be blue in a few weeks; and fiddle-heads everywhere. There will be no end of ferns. May to any extent—it's only in bud yet—and there's a wren's nest in there. . . .' At this point he rolled suddenly over on to his back and looked up.

'A lark,' he explained. 'There was one singing its head off this morning. I say, Dick, this will be a good field for a kite, won't it? *But wait a bit.*'

After every fresh thing that Sandy showed us in our field, he always finished by saying, '*Wait a bit*'; and that was because there was always something else better still.

'There's a brook at the bottom there,' he said, 'with lots of freshwater shrimps. I wonder whether they would boil red. *But wait a bit.* This hedge, you see, has got a very high bank, and it's worn into kind of ledges. I think we could play at "shops" there—*but wait a bit.*'

'It's almost *too* good, Sandy dear!' said I, as we crossed the field to the opposite hedge.

'The best is to come,' said Sandy. 'I've a very good mind not to let it out till to-morrow.' And to our distraction he sat down in the middle of the field, put his arms around his knees, as if we were playing at 'Honey-pots,' and rocked himself backwards and for-wards with a face of brimming satisfaction.

Neither Richard nor I would have been so mean as to explore on our own account when the field was Sandy's discovery, but we tried hard to persuade him to show us everything.

He had the most provoking way of laughing and holding his tongue, and he did that now, besides slowly turning all his pockets inside out into his hands, and mumbling up the crumbs and odd currants, saying: 'Guess!' between every mouthful.

But when there was not a crumb left in the seams of his pockets, Sandy turned them back, and jumping up, said: 'One can only tell a secret once. It's a hollow oak. Come along!'

He ran and we ran, to the other side of Our Field. I had read of hollow oaks, and seen pictures of them, and once I dreamed of one, with a witch inside, but we had never had one to play in. We were nearly wild with delight. It looked all solid from the field, but when we pushed behind, on the hedge side, there was the door, and I crept in, and it smelt of wood, and delicious damp. There could not be a more perfect castle, and though there were no windows in the sides, the light came in from the top, where the ferns hung over like a fringe. Sandy was quite right. It was the very best thing in Our Field.

Perronet was as fond of the field as we were. What he liked were the little birds. At least, I don't know that he liked them, but they were what he chiefly attended to. I think he knew that it was our field, and thought he was the watch-dog of it, and whenever a bird settled down anywhere, he barked at it, and then it flew away, and he ran barking after it till he lost it; and by that time another had settled down, and then Perronet flew at him, and so on, all up and down the hedge. He never caught a bird, and never would let one sit down, if he could see it.

We had all kinds of games in Our Field. Shops—for there were quantities of things to sell—and sometimes I was a moss-merchant, for there were ten different kinds of moss by the brook, and sometimes I was a jeweller, and sold daisy-chains and pebbles, and coral sets made of holly berries, and oak-apple necklaces; and sometimes I kept provisions, like earth-nuts, and mallow-cheeses, and mushrooms; and sometimes I kept a flower-shop, and sold nosegays and wreaths, and umbrellas made of rushes. I liked that kind of shop, because I am fond of arranging flowers, and I always make our birthday wreaths. And sometimes I kept a whole lot of shops, and Richard and Sandy bought my things, and paid for them with money made of elder-pith, sliced into rounds. The first shop I kept was to sell cowslips, and Richard and Sandy lived by the brook, and were wine merchants, and made cowslip wine in a tin mug.

The elder-tree was a beauty. In July the cream-coloured flowers were so sweet, we could hardly sit under it, and in the autumn it was covered with berries; but we were always a little disappointed that they never tasted in the least like elderberry syrup. Richard used to make flutes out of the stalks, and he could really play tunes on one of them, but it always made Perronet bark.

Richard's every-day cap had a large hole in the top, and when we were in Our Field we always hung it on the top of the tallest of the two stile-posts, to show that we were there; just as the Queen has a flag hung out at Windsor Castle, when she is at home.

We played at castles and houses, and when we were tired of the houses, we pretended to pack up, and went to the sea-side for a change of air by the brook. Sandy and I took off our shoes and stockings and were bathing-women, and we bathed Perronet; and Richard sat on the bank and was a 'tripper,' looking at us through a telescope; for when the elder-stems cracked and wouldn't do for flutes he made them into telescopes. And before we went down to the brook we made jam of hips and haws from the hedge at the top of the field, and put it into acorn cups, and took it with us, that the children might not be short of roly-polies at the seaside.

Whatever we played at we were never disturbed. Birds and cows, and men and horses ploughing in the distance, do not disturb you at all.

We were very happy that summer: the boys were quite happy, and the only thing that vexed me was thinking of Perronet's tax-money. For months and months went on and we did not save it. Once we got as far as twopence halfpenny, and then one day Richard came to me and said: 'I must have some more string for the kite. You might lend me a penny out of Perronet's stocking, till I get some money of my own.'

So I did; and the next day Sandy came and said: 'You lent Dick one of Perronet's coppers; I'm sure Perronet would lend me one,' and then they said it was ridiculous to leave a halfpenny there by itself, so we spent it on acid drops.

It worried me so much at last, that I began to dream horrible dreams about Perronet having to go away because we hadn't saved his tax-money. And then I used to wake up and cry, till the pillow was so wet, I had to turn it. The boys never seemed to mind, but then boys don't think about things; so that I was quite surprised when one day I found Sandy alone in our field with Perronet in his arms, crying, and feeding him with cake; and I found he was crying about the tax-money.

I cannot bear to see boys cry. I would much rather cry myself, and I begged Sandy to leave off, for I said I was quite determined to try and think of something.

It certainly was remarkable that the very next day should be the day when we heard about the flower-show.

It was in school—the village school, for mother could not afford to send us anywhere else—and the schoolmaster rapped on his desk and said: 'Silence, children!' and that at the agricultural show there was to be a flower show this year, and that an old gentleman was going to give prizes to the school-children for window-plants and for the best arranged wild flowers. There were to be nosegays and wreaths, and there was to be a first prize of five shillings, and a second prize of half a crown, for the best collection of wild flowers with the names put to them.

'The English names,' said the schoolmaster; 'and there may be —silence, children!—there may be collections of ferns, or grasses, or mosses to compete, too, for the gentleman wishes to encourage a taste for natural history.'

And several of the village children said: 'What's that?' and I squeezed Sandy's arm, who was sitting next to me, and whispered: 'Five shillings!' and the schoolmaster said: 'Silence, children!' and I thought I never should have finished my lessons that day for thinking of Perronet's tax-money.

July is not at all a good month for wild flowers; May and June are far better. However, the show was to be in the first week of July.

I said to the boys: 'Look here: I'll do a collection of flowers. I know the names, and I can print. It's no good two or three people muddling with arranging flowers; but if you will get me what I want, I shall be very much obliged. If either of you will make another collection, you know there are ten kinds of mosses by the brook; and we have names for them of our own, and they are English. Perhaps they'll do. But everything must come out of Our Field.'

The boys agreed, and they were very good. Richard made me a box, rather high at the back. We put sand at the bottom and damped it, and then Feather Moss, lovely clumps of it, and into that I stuck the flowers. They all came out of Our Field. I like to see grass with flowers, and we had very pretty grasses, and between every bunch of flowers I put a bunch of grass of different kinds. I got all the flowers and the grasses ready first, and printed the names on pieces of cardboard to stick in with them, and then I arranged them by my eye, and Sandy handed me what I called for, for Richard was busy at the Brook making a tray of mosses.

Sandy knew the flowers and the names of them quite as well as I did, of course; we knew everything that lived in Our Field; so when I called: 'Ox-eye daisies, cock's-foot grass, labels; meadow-sweet, fox-tail grass, labels; dog-roses, shivering grass, labels'; and so on, he gave me the right things, and I had nothing to do but to put the colours that looked best together next to each other, and to make the grass look light, and pull up bits of the moss to show well. And at the very end I put in a label: 'All out of Our Field.'

I did not like it when it was done; but Richard praised it so much, it cheered me up, and I thought his mosses looked lovely.

The flower-show day was very hot. I did not think it could be hotter anywhere in the world than it was in the field where the show was; but it was hotter in the tent.

We should never have got in at all—for you had to pay at the gate—but they let competitors in free, though not at first. When we got in, there were a lot of grown-up people, and it was very hard work getting along among them, and getting to see the stands with the things on. We kept seeing tickets with '1st Prize' and '2nd Prize,' and struggling up; but they were sure to be dahlias in a tray, or fruit that you mightn't eat, or vegetables. The vegetables disappointed us so often, I got to hate them. I don't think I shall ever like very big potatoes (before they are boiled) again, particularly the red ones. It makes me feel sick with heat and anxiety to think of them.

It was a picnic tea, and we had it in Our Field.

We had struggled slowly all round the tent, and seen all the cucumbers, onions, lettuces, long potatoes, round potatoes, and everything else, when we saw an old gentleman, with spectacles and white hair, standing with two or three ladies. And then we saw three nosegays in jugs, with all the green picked off, and the flowers tied as tightly together as they would go, and then we saw some prettier ones, and then we saw my collection, and it had got a big label in it marked '1st Prize,' and next to it came Richard's moss-tray, with the Hair-moss, and the Pincushion-moss, and the Scale-mosses, and a lot of others with names of our own, and it was marked '2nd Prize.' And I gripped one of Sandy's arms just as Richard seized the other, and we all cried, 'Perronet is paid for!'

There was two and sixpence over. We never had such a feast! It was a picnic tea, and we had it in Our Field. I thought Sandy and Perronet would have died of cake, but they were none the worse.

We were very much frightened at first when the old gentleman invited himself; but he would come, and he brought a lot of nuts, and he did get inside the oak, though it is really too small for him.

I don't think there ever was anybody so kind. If he were not a man, I should really and truly believe in Sandy's fairy godmother.

Of course I don't really believe in fairies. I am not so young as that. And I know that Our Field does not exactly belong to us.

I wonder to whom it does belong? Richard says he believes it belongs to the gentleman who lives at the big red house among the trees. But he must be wrong; for we see that gentleman at church every Sunday, but we never saw him in Our Field.

And I don't believe anybody could have such a field of their very own and never come to see it, from one end of summer to the other.

From *The Brownies and Other Stories*
by Juliana H. Ewing

THE UGLY DUCKLING

HANS CHRISTIAN ANDERSEN

IT WAS so beautiful out in the country. It was summer—the wheat fields were golden, the oats were green, and down among the green meadows the hay was stacked. There the stork minced about on his red legs, clacking away in Egyptian, which was the language his mother had taught him. Round about the field and meadow lands rose vast forests, in which deep lakes lay hidden. Yes, it was indeed lovely out there in the country.

In the midst of the sunshine there stood an old manor house that had a deep moat around it. From the walls of the manor right down to the water's edge great burdock leaves grew, and there were some so tall that little children could stand upright beneath the biggest of them. In this wilderness of leaves, which was as dense as the forest itself, a duck sat on her nest, hatching her ducklings. She was becoming somewhat weary, because sitting is such a dull business and scarcely anyone came to see her. The other ducks would much rather swim in the moat than waddle out and squat under a burdock leaf to gossip with her.

But at last the eggshells began to crack, one after another. "Peep, peep!" said the little things, as they came to life and poked out their heads.

"Quack, quack!" said the duck, and quick as quick can be they all waddled out to have a look at the green world under the leaves. Their mother let them look as much as they pleased, because green is good for the eyes.

"How wide the world is," said all the young ducks, for they certainly had much more room now than they had when they were in their eggshells.

"Do you think this is the whole world?" their mother asked. "Why it extends on and on, clear across to the other side of the garden and right on into the parson's field, though that is further than I have ever been. I do hope you are all hatched," she said as she got up. "No, not quite all. The biggest egg still lies here. How much longer is this going to take? I am really rather tired of it all," she said, but she settled back on her nest.

"Well, how goes it?" asked an old duck who came to pay her a call.

"It takes a long time with that one egg," said the duck on the nest. "It won't crack, but look at the others. They are the cutest little ducklings I've ever seen. They look exactly like their father, the wretch! He hasn't come to see me at all."

"Let's have a look at the egg that won't crack," the old duck said. "It's a turkey egg, and you can take my word for it. I was fooled like that once myself. What trouble and care I had with those turkey children, for I may as well tell you, they are afraid of the water. I simply could not get them into it. I quacked and snapped at them, but it wasn't a bit of use. Let me see the egg. Certainly, it's a turkey egg. Let it lie, and go teach your other children to swim."

"Oh, I'll sit a little longer. I've been at it so long already that I may as well sit here half the summer."

"Suit yourself," said the old duck, and away she waddled.

At last the big egg did crack. "Peep," said the young one, and out he tumbled, but he was so big and ugly.

The duck took a look at him. "That's a frightfully big duckling," she said. "He doesn't look the least like the others. Can he really be a turkey baby? Well, well! I'll soon find out. Into the water he shall go, even if I have to shove him in myself."

Next day the weather was perfectly splendid, and the sun shone down on all the green burdock leaves. The mother duck led her whole family down to the moat. Splash! she took to the water. "Quack, quack," said she, and one duckling after another plunged in. The water went over their heads, but they came up in a flash, and floated to perfection. Their legs worked automatically, and they were all there in the water. Even the big, ugly gray one was swimming along.

"Why, that's no turkey," she said. "See how nicely he uses his legs, and how straight he holds himself. He's my very own son after all, and quite good-looking if you look at him properly. Quack, quack, come with me. I'll lead you out into the world and introduce you to the duck yard. But keep close to me so that you won't get stepped on, and watch out for the cat!"

Thus they sallied into the duck yard, where all was in an uproar because two families were fighting over the head of an eel. But the cat got it, after all.

"You see, that's the way of the world." The mother duck licked her bill because she wanted the eel's head for herself. "Stir your legs. Bustle about, and mind that you bend your necks to that old duck over there. She's the noblest of us all, and has Spanish blood in her. That's why she's so fat. See that red rag around her leg? That's a wonderful thing, and the highest distinction a duck can get. It shows that they don't want to lose her, and that she's to have special attention from man and beast. Shake yourselves! Don't turn your toes in. A well-bred duckling turns his toes way out, just as his father and mother do—this way. So then! Now duck your necks and say quack!"

They did as she told them, but the other ducks around them looked on and said right out loud, "See here! Must we have this brood too, just as if there weren't enough of us already? And—fie! what an ugly-looking fellow that duckling is! We won't stand for him." One duck charged up and bit his neck.

"Let him alone," his mother said. "He isn't doing any harm."

"Possibly not," said the duck who bit him, "but he's too big and strange, and therefore he needs a good whacking."

"What nice-looking children you have, Mother," said the old duck with the rag around her leg. "They are all pretty except that one. He didn't come out so well. It's a pity you can't hatch him again."

"That can't be managed, your ladyship," said the mother. "He isn't so handsome, but he's as good as can be, and he swims just as well as the rest, or, I should say, even a little better than they do. I hope his looks will improve with age, and after a while he won't seem so big. He took too long in the egg, and that's why his figure isn't all that it should be." She pinched his neck and preened his feathers. "Moreover, he's a drake, so it won't matter so much. I think he will be quite strong, and I'm sure he will amount to something."

"The other ducklings are pretty enough," said the old duck. "Now make yourselves right at home, and if you find an eel's head you may bring it to me."

So they felt quite at home. But the poor duckling who had been the last one out of his egg, and who looked so ugly, was pecked and pushed about and made fun of by the ducks, and the chickens as well. "He's too big," said they all. The turkey gobbler, who thought himself an emperor because he was born wearing spurs, puffed up like a ship under full sail and bore down upon him, gobbling and gobbling until he was red in the face. The poor duckling did not know where he dared stand or where he dared walk. He was so sad because he was so desperately ugly, and because he was the laughing stock of the whole barnyard.

So it went on the first day, and after that things went from bad to worse. The poor duckling was chased and buffeted about by everyone. Even his own brothers and sisters abused him. "Oh," they would always say, "how we wish the cat would catch you, you ugly thing." And his mother said, "How I do wish you were miles away." The ducks nipped him, and the hens pecked him, and the girl who fed them kicked him with her foot.

So he ran away; and he flew over the fence. The little birds in the bushes darted up in a fright. "That's because I'm so ugly," he thought, and closed his eyes, but he ran on just the same until he reached the great marsh where the wild ducks lived. There he lay all night long, weary and disheartened.

When morning came, the wild ducks flew up to have a look at their new companion. "What sort of creature are you?" they asked, as the duckling turned in all directions, bowing his best to them all. "You are terribly ugly," they told him, "but that's nothing to us so long as you don't marry into our family."

Poor duckling! Marriage certainly had never entered his mind. All he wanted was for them to let him lie among the reeds and drink a little water from the marsh.

There he stayed for two whole days. Then he met two wild geese, or rather wild ganders—for they were males. They had not been out of the shell very long, and that's what made them so sure of themselves.

"Say there, comrade," they said, "you're so ugly that we have taken a fancy to you. Come with us and be a bird of passage. In another marsh near-by, there are some fetching wild geese, all nice young ladies who know how to quack. You are so ugly that you'll completely turn their heads."

Bing! Bang! Shots rang in the air, and these two ganders fell dead among the reeds. The water was red with their blood. *Bing! Bang!* the shots rang, and as whole flocks of wild geese flew up from the reeds another volley crashed. A great hunt was in progress. The hunters lay under cover all around the marsh, and some even perched on branches of trees that overhung the reeds. Blue smoke rose like clouds from the shade of the trees, and drifted far out over the water.

The bird dogs came *splash, splash!* through the swamp, bending down the reeds and the rushes on every side. This gave the poor duckling such a fright that he twisted his head about to hide it under his wing. But at that very moment a fearfully big dog appeared right beside him. His tongue lolled out of his mouth and his wicked eyes glared horribly. He opened his wide jaws, flashed his sharp teeth, and—*splash, splash*—on he went without touching the duckling.

"Thank heavens," he sighed, "I'm so ugly that the dog won't even bother to bite me."

He lay perfectly still, while the bullets splattered through the reeds as shot after shot was fired. It was late in the day before things became quiet again, and even then the poor duckling didn't dare move. He waited several hours before he ventured to look about him, and then he scurried away from that marsh as fast as he could go. He ran across field and meadows. The wind was so strong that he had to struggle to keep his feet.

Late in the evening he came to a miserable little hovel, so ramshackle that it did not know which way to tumble, and that was the only reason it still stood. The wind struck the duckling so hard that the poor little fellow had to sit down on his tail to withstand it. The storm blew stronger and stronger, but the duckling noticed that one hinge had come loose and the door hung so crooked that he could squeeze through the crack into the room, and that's just what he did.

Here lived an old women with her cat and her hen. The cat, whom she called "Sonny," could arch his back, purr, and even make sparks, though for that you had to stroke his fur the wrong way. The hen had short little legs, so she was called "Chickey Shortleg." She laid good eggs, and the old woman loved her as if she had been her own child.

In the morning they were quick to notice the strange duckling. The cat began to purr, and the hen began to cluck.

"What on earth!" The old woman looked around, but she was short-sighted, and she mistook the duckling for a fat duck that had lost its way. "That was a good catch," she said. "Now I shall have duck eggs—unless it's a drake. We must try it out." So the duckling was tried out for three weeks, but not one egg did he lay.

In this house the cat was master and the hen was mistress. They always said, "We and the world," for they thought themselves half of the world, and much the better half at that. The duckling thought that there might be more than one way of thinking, but the hen would not hear of it.

"Can you lay eggs?" she asked.

"No."

"Then be so good as to hold your tongue."

The cat asked, "Can you arch your back, purr, or make sparks?"

"No."

"Then keep your opinion to yourself when sensible people are talking."

The duckling sat in a corner, feeling most despondent. Then he remembered the fresh air and the sunlight. Such a desire to go swimming on the water possessed him that he could not help telling the hen about it.

"What on earth has come over you?" the hen cried. "You haven't a thing to do, and that's why you get such silly notions. Lay us an egg, or learn to purr, and you'll get over it."

"But it's so refreshing to float on the water," said the duckling, "so refreshing to feel it rise over your head as you dive to the bottom."

"Yes, it must be a great pleasure!" said the hen. "I think you must have gone crazy. Ask the cat, who's the wisest fellow I know, whether he likes to swim or dive down in the water. Of myself I say nothing. But ask the old woman, our mistress. There's no one on earth wiser than she is. Do you imagine she wants to go swimming and feel the water rise over her head?"

"You don't understand me," said the duckling.

"Well, if we don't, who would? Surely you don't think you are cleverer than the cat and the old woman—to say nothing of myself. Don't be so conceited, child. Just thank your Maker for all the kindness we have shown you. Didn't you get into this snug room, and fall in with people who can tell you what's what? But you are such a numbskull that it's no pleasure to have you around. Believe me, I tell you this for your own good. I say unpleasant truths, but that's the only way you can know who are your friends. Be sure now that you lay some eggs. See to it that you learn to purr or to make sparks."

"I think I'd better go out into the wide world," said the duckling.

"Suit yourself," said the hen.

So off went the duckling. He swam on the water, and dived down in it, but still he was slighted by every living creature because of his ugliness.

Autumn came on. The leaves in the forest turned yellow and brown. The wind took them and whirled them about. The heavens looked cold as the low clouds hung heavy with snow and hail. Perched on the fence, the raven screamed, "Caw, caw!" and trembled with cold. It made one shiver to think of it. Pity the poor little duckling.

One evening, just as the sun was setting in splendor, a great flock of large, handsome birds appeared out of the reeds. The duckling had never seen birds so beautiful. They were dazzling white, with long graceful necks. They were swans. They uttered a very strange cry as they unfurled their magnificent wings to fly from this cold land, away to warmer countries and to open waters. They went up so high, so very high, that the ugly little duckling felt a strange uneasiness come over him as he watched them. He went around and round in the water, like a wheel. He craned his neck to follow their course, and gave a cry so shrill and strange that he frightened himself. Oh! He could not forget them—those splendid, happy birds. When he could no longer see them he dived to the very bottom, and when he came up again he was quite beside himself. He did not know what birds they were or whither they were bound, yet he loved them more than anything he had ever loved before. It was not that he envied them, for how could he ever dare dream of wanting their marvelous beauty for himself? He would have been grateful if only the ducks would have tolerated him—the poor ugly creature.

The winter grew cold—so bitterly cold that the duckling had to swim to and fro in the water to keep it from freezing over. But every night the hole in which he swam kept getting smaller and smaller. Then it froze so hard that the duckling had to paddle continuously to keep the crackling ice from closing in upon him. At last, too tired to move, he was frozen fast in the ice.

Early that morning a farmer came by, and when he saw how things were he went out on the pond, broke away the ice with his wooden shoe, and carried the duckling home to his wife. There the duckling revived, but when the children wished to play with him he thought they meant to hurt him. Terrified, he fluttered into the milk pail, splashing the whole room with milk. The woman shrieked and threw up her hands as he flew into the butter tub, and then in and out of the meal barrel. Imagine what he looked like now! The woman screamed and lashed out at him with the fire tongs. The children tumbled over each other as they tried to catch him, and they laughed and they shouted. Luckily the door was open, and the duckling escaped through it into the bushes, where he lay down, in the newly fallen snow, as if in a daze.

But it would be too sad to tell of all the hardships and wretchedness he had to endure during this cruel winter. When the warm sun shone once more, the duckling was still alive among the reeds

From the thicket before him came three lovely white swans.

of the marsh. The larks began to sing again. It was beautiful springtime.

Then, quite suddenly, he lifted his wings. They swept through the air much more strongly than before, and their powerful strokes carried him far. Before he quite knew what was happening, he found himself in a great garden where apple trees bloomed. The lilacs filled the air with sweet scent and hung in clusters from long, green branches that bent over a winding stream. Oh, but it was lovely here in the freshness of spring!

From the thicket before him came three lovely white swans. They ruffled their feathers and swam lightly in the stream. The duckling recognized these noble creatures, and a strange feeling of sadness came upon him.

"I shall fly near these royal birds, and they will peck me to bits because I, who am so very ugly, dare to go near them. But I don't care. Better be killed by them than to be nipped by the ducks, pecked by the hens, kicked about by the henyard girl, or suffer such misery in winter."

So he flew into the water and swam toward the splendid swans. They saw him, and swept down upon him with their rustling feathers raised. "Kill me!" said the poor creature, and he bowed his head down over the water to wait for death. But what did he see there, mirrored in the clear stream? He beheld his own image, and it was no longer the reflection of a clumsy, dirty, gray bird, ugly and offensive. He himself was a swan! Being born in a duck yard does not matter, if only you are hatched from a swan's egg.

He felt quite glad that he had come through so much trouble and misfortune, for now he had a fuller understanding of his own good fortune, and of beauty when he met with it. The great swans swam all around him and stroked him with their bills.

Several little children came into the garden to throw grain and bits of bread upon the water. The smallest child cried, "Here's a new one," and the others rejoiced, "yes, a new one has come." They clapped their hands, danced around, and ran to bring their father and mother.

And they threw bread and cake upon the water, while they all agreed, "The new one is the most handsome of all. He's so young and so good-looking." The old swans bowed in his honor.

Then he felt very bashful, and tucked his head under his wing. He did not know what this was all about. He felt so very happy, but he wasn't at all proud, for a good heart never grows proud. He thought about how he had been persecuted and scorned, and now he heard them all call him the most beautiful of all beautiful birds. The lilacs dipped their clusters into the stream before him, and the sun shone so warm and so heartening. He rustled his feathers and held his slender neck high, as he cried out with full heart: "I never dreamed there could be so much happiness, when I was the ugly duckling."

DATE DUE

JY 19'67			
JY 31 67			
APR 14 '69			
SEP 29 '69			
SE 24 '70			
NO 14 '74			
MAY 04 '80			
GAYLORD			PRINTED IN U.S.A.